Infinity Prime Donna Casey

"This fractal is a classic spiral, which is my favorite, and I'm always amazed at the variations and the endlessly repeating patterns that can be created out of such a primary shape." — **Donna Casey**

Measuring and Counting

Measurement and the Number System 2   **UNIT 4**

Investigations

IN NUMBER, DATA, AND SPACE®

Editorial offices: Glenview, Illinois • Parsippany, New Jersey • New York, New York
Sales offices: Boston, Massachusetts • Duluth, Georgia
Glenview, Illinois • Coppell, Texas • Sacramento, California • Mesa, Arizona

The Investigations curriculum was developed by TERC, Cambridge, MA.

TERC

This material is based on work supported by the National Science Foundation ("NSF") under Grant No. ESI-0095450. Any opinions, findings, and conclusions or recommendations expressed in this material are those of the author(s) and do not necessarily reflect the views of the National Science Foundation.

ISBN: 0-328-23723-X

ISBN: 978-0-328-23723-4

8 9 10-V003-15 14 13 12 11 10 09 08

CC:N3

T E R C

Co-Principal Investigators

Susan Jo Russell

Karen Economopoulos

Authors

Lucy Wittenberg
Director Grades 3–5

Karen Economopoulos
Director Grades K–2

Virginia Bastable
(SummerMath for Teachers,
Mt. Holyoke College)

Katie Hickey Bloomfield

Keith Cochran

Darrell Earnest

Arusha Hollister

Nancy Horowitz

Erin Leidl

Megan Murray

Young Oh

Beth W. Perry

Susan Jo Russell

Deborah Schifter
(Education
Development Center)

Kathy Sillman

Administrative Staff

Amy Taber
Project Manager

Beth Bergeron

Lorraine Brooks

Emi Fujiwara

Contributing Authors

Denise Baumann

Jennifer DiBrienza

Hollee Freeman

Paula Hooper

Jan Mokros

Stephen Monk
(University of Washington)

Mary Beth O'Connor

Judy Storeygard

Cornelia Tierney

Elizabeth Van Cleef

Carol Wright

Technology

Jim Hammerman

Classroom Field Work

Amy Appell

Rachel E. Davis

Traci Higgins

Julia Thompson

Collaborating Teachers

This group of dedicated teachers carried out extensive field testing in their classrooms, met regularly to discuss issues of teaching and learning mathematics, provided feedback to staff, welcomed staff into their classrooms to document students' work, and contributed both suggestions and written material that has been incorporated into the curriculum.

Bethany Altchek

Linda Amaral

Kimberly Beauregard

Barbara Bernard

Nancy Buell

Rose Christiansen

Chris Colbath-Hess

Lisette Colon

Kim Cook

Frances Cooper

Kathleen Drew

Rebeka Eston Salemi

Thomas Fisher

Michael Flynn

Holly Ghazey

Susan Gillis

Danielle Harrington

Elaine Herzog

Francine Hiller

Kirsten Lee Howard

Liliana Klass

Leslie Kramer

Melissa Lee Andrichak

Kelley Lee Sadowski

Jennifer Levitan

Mary Lou LoVecchio

Kristen McEnaney

Maura McGrail

Kathe Millett

Florence Molyneaux

Amy Monkiewicz

Elizabeth Monopoli

Carol Murray

Robyn Musser

Christine Norrman

Deborah O'Brien

Timothy O'Connor

Anne Marie O'Reilly

Mark Paige

Margaret Riddle

Karen Schweitzer

Elisabeth Seyferth

Susan Smith

Debra Sorvillo

Shoshanah Starr

Janice Szymaszek

Karen Tobin

JoAnn Trauschke

Ana Vaisenstein

Yvonne Watson

Michelle Woods

Mary Wright

Note: Unless otherwise noted, all contributors listed above were staff of the Education Research Collaborative at TERC during their work on the curriculum. Other affiliations during the time of development are listed.

Advisors

Deborah Lowenberg Ball,
University of Michigan

Hyman Bass, Professor of Mathematics and Mathematics Education
University of Michigan

Mary Canner, Principal, Natick Public Schools

Thomas Carpenter, Professor of Curriculum and Instruction,
University of Wisconsin-Madison

Janis Freckmann, Elementary Mathematics Coordinator,
Milwaukee Public Schools

Lynne Godfrey, Mathematics Coach,
Cambridge Public Schools

Ginger Hanlon, Instructional Specialist in Mathematics,
New York City Public Schools

DeAnn Huinker, Director, Center for Mathematics and
Science Education Research, University of Wisconsin-Milwaukee

James Kaput, Professor of Mathematics, University of
Massachusetts-Dartmouth

Kate Kline, Associate Professor, Department of Mathematics
and Statistics, Western Michigan University

Jim Lewis, Professor of Mathematics,
University of Nebraska-Lincoln

William McCallum, Professor of Mathematics,
University of Arizona

Harriet Pollatsek, Professor of Mathematics,
Mount Holyoke College

Debra Shein-Gerson, Elementary Mathematics Specialist,
Weston Public Schools

Gary Shevell, Assistant Principal,
New York City Public Schools

Liz Sweeney, Elementary Math Department,
Boston Public Schools

Lucy West, Consultant, Metamorphosis:
Teaching Learning Communities, Inc.

This revision of the curriculum was built on the work of the many authors who contributed to the first edition (published between 1994 and 1998). We acknowledge the critical contributions of these authors in developing the content and pedagogy of *Investigations*:

Authors

Joan Akers

Michael T. Battista

Douglas H. Clements

Karen Economopoulos

Marlene Kliman

Jan Mokros

Megan Murray

Ricardo Nemirovsky

Andee Rubin

Susan Jo Russell

Cornelia Tierney

Contributing Authors

Mary Berle-Carman

Rebecca B. Corwin

Rebeka Eston

Claryce Evans

Anne Goodrow

Cliff Konold

Chris Mainhart

Sue McMillen

Jerrie Moffet

Tracy Noble

Kim O'Neil

Mark Ogonowski

Julie Sarama

Amy Shulman Weinberg

Margie Singer

Virginia Woolley

Tracey Wright

Contents

UNIT 4

Measuring and Counting

Investigations

CURRICULUM

Overview of Program Components

FOR TEACHERS

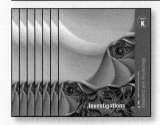

The **Curriculum Units** are the teaching guides. (See far right.)

Implementing Investigations in Kindergarten offers suggestions for implementing the curriculum. It also contains a comprehensive index.

The **Resources Binder** contains all the Resource Masters that support instruction. (Also available on CD) The binder also includes a student software CD.

FOR STUDENTS

The **Student Activity Book** contains the consumable student pages (Recording Sheets, Homework, Practice, and so on).

The **Student Math Handbook Flip Chart** contains pictures of Math Words and Ideas pages.

The *Investigations* Curriculum

Investigations in Number, Data, and Space® is a K–5 mathematics curriculum designed to engage students in making sense of mathematical ideas. Six major goals guided the development of the *Investigations in Number, Data, and Space®* curriculum. The curriculum is designed to:

- Support students to make sense of mathematics and learn that they can be mathematical thinkers

- Focus on computational fluency with whole numbers as a major goal of the elementary grades

- Provide substantive work in important areas of mathematics—rational numbers, geometry, measurement, data, and early algebra—and connections among them

- Emphasize reasoning about mathematical ideas

- Communicate mathematics content and pedagogy to teachers

- Engage the range of learners in understanding mathematics

Underlying these goals are three guiding principles that are touchstones for the *Investigations* team as we approach both students and teachers as agents of their own learning:

1. *Students have mathematical ideas.* Students come to school with ideas about numbers, shapes, measurements, patterns, and data. If given the opportunity to learn in an environment that stresses making sense of mathematics, students build on the ideas they already have and learn about new mathematics they have never encountered. Students learn that they are capable of having mathematical ideas, applying what they know to new situations, and thinking and reasoning about unfamiliar problems.

2. *Teachers are engaged in ongoing learning* about mathematics content, pedagogy, and student learning. The curriculum provides material for professional development, to be used by teachers individually or in groups, that supports teachers' continued learning as they use the curriculum over several years. The *Investigations* curriculum materials are designed as much to be a dialogue with teachers as to be a core of content for students.

3. *Teachers collaborate with the students and curriculum materials* to create the curriculum as enacted in the classroom. The only way for a good curriculum to be used well is for teachers to be active participants in implementing it. Teachers use the curriculum to maintain a clear, focused, and coherent agenda for mathematics teaching. At the same time, they observe and listen carefully to students, try to understand how they are thinking, and make teaching decisions based on these observations.

Investigations is based on experience from research and practice, including field testing that involved documentation of thousands of hours in classrooms, observations of students, input from teachers, and analysis of student work. As a result, the curriculum addresses the learning needs of real students in a wide range of classrooms and communities. The investigations are carefully designed to invite all students into mathematics—girls and boys; members of diverse cultural, ethnic, and language groups; and students with a wide variety of strengths, needs, and interests.

Based on this extensive classroom testing, the curriculum takes seriously the time students need to develop a strong conceptual foundation and skills based on that foundation. Each curriculum unit focuses on an area of content in depth, providing time for students to develop and practice ideas across a variety of activities and contexts that build on each other. Daily guidelines for time spent on class sessions, Classroom Routines (K–3), and Ten-Minute Math (3–5) reflect the commitment to devoting adequate time to mathematics in each school day.

About This Curriculum Unit

This **Curriculum Unit** is the fourth of seven teaching guides in Grade K. The fourth unit in Grade K is *Measuring and Counting*.

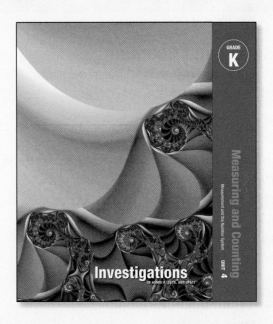

- The **Introduction and Overview** section organizes and presents the instructional materials, provides background information, and highlights important features specific to this unit.

- Each Curriculum Unit contains several **Investigations.** Each Investigation focuses on a set of related mathematical ideas.

- Investigations are divided into 30–45 minute **Sessions,** or lessons.

- Sessions have a combination of these parts: **Activity, Discussion, Math Workshop,** and **Session Follow-Up.**

- Each session also has one or more **Classroom Routines** that are done outside of math time.

- At the back of the book is a collection of **Teacher Notes** and **Dialogue Boxes** that provide professional development related to the unit.

- Also included at the back of the book are the **Student Math Handbook Flip Chart** pages for this unit.

- The **Index** provides a way to look up important words or terms.

Overview

O F T H I S U N I T

Investigation	Session	Day	
INVESTIGATION 1 **Measuring and Counting** Students use cubes and craft sticks to measure and compare the lengths of shoes, strips of tape, and other objects.	**1.1** Measuring Our Shoes	1	
	1.2 Measuring Different Shoe Lengths	2	
	1.3 Measuring with Sticks	3	
	1.4 Comparing Lengths of Shoes	4	
	1.5 Measuring with Cubes	5	
INVESTIGATION 2 **Counting Some, Counting More** Students continue to count and measure. They develop strategies for finding the total after a small amount is added to a set.	**2.1** Revisiting Counting	6	
	2.2 Collect 10 Together	7	
	2.3 Build On	8	
	2.4 Roll and Record 2	9	
	2.5 Quick Images: Ten-Frames	10	
INVESTIGATION 3 **Changing Quantities: How Many Now?** Students act out story problems and play games that involve counting, comparing, and finding the total when a small amount is added or taken away.	**3.1** Racing Bears	11	
	3.2 Story Problems	12	
	3.3 One More, One Fewer	13	
	3.4 Double Compare	14	
	3.5 More or Less at the End?	15	
	3.6 Build It/Change It	16	
	3.7 Who Has More?	17	

Each *Investigations* session has some combination of these four parts: **Activity, Discussion, Math Workshop,** and **Session Follow-Up.** These session parts are indicated in the chart below. Each session also has one or more **Classroom Routines** that are done outside of math time.

Activity	Discussion	Math Workshop	Assessment Checklist*	Session Follow-Up
••	•		•	•
•	•	•		•
•	•	•		•
	•	•		•
•	•	•		•
••	•	•	•	•
••	•	•		•
•	•	•		•
••	•			•
•	•	•		•
••	•			•
•	•	•		•
••		•	•	•
••		•		•
	•	•		•
•	•	•		•
•	•	•		•

Classroom Routines

Calendar	Attendance	Today's Question	Patterns on the Pocket Chart
	•		
•			
		•	
			•
	•		
•			
		•	
			•
	•		
•			
		•	
			•
	•		
•			
		•	
•			
	•		

*An Assessment Checklist is introduced in this session.

Overview

O F   T H I S   U N I T

Investigation	Session	Day	
INVESTIGATION 4 **Ways to Make Numbers** Students explore different ways to compose and decompose numbers as they view, create, and re-create arrangements for the numbers to 10.	**4.1** Six Tiles in All	18	
	4.2 Quick Images: Square Tiles	19	
	4.3 Arrangements of 5 to 10 Tiles	20	
	4.4 Toss the Chips	21	
	4.5 Quick Images in Pairs	22	
	4.6 Combinations of 6	23	
	4.7 Arrangements of 6	24	
	4.8 End-of-Unit Assessment and Arrangements of Numbers	25	
	4.9 End-of-Unit Assessment and Arrangements of 7	26	

Activity	Discussion	Math Workshop	Assessment Checklist*	Session Follow-Up
●●	●			●
●●		●		●
●	●	●		●
●●		●		●
●●		●		●
	●	●		●
●	●●	●		●
	●	●		●
	●	●		●

Classroom Routines

Calendar	Attendance	Today's Question	Patterns on the Pocket Chart
●			
		●	
			●
		●	
●			
		●	
			●
●			
	●		

*An Assessment Checklist is introduced in this session.

Mathematics

IN THIS UNIT

Measuring and Counting is the fourth of seven units in the Kindergarten sequence, and the second of three units in the Kindergarten number strand. These units develop ideas about counting and quantity, comparison, linear measurement, the composition of numbers, and the operations of addition and subtraction. The mathematical focus of this unit is on using multiple nonstandard units to measure length, counting sets of objects, finding the total after a small amount is added to (or taken away from) a set of objects, and figuring out what needs to be added to (or taken away from) a set in order to make a set of a given size. Students begin making sense of the operations of addition and subtraction as they act out stories and play games that involve combining or separating small amounts. Students also create and recreate a wide range of images for the quantities up to 10 by finding many different ways to arrange a set of square tiles.

 LOOKING BACK This unit builds on the work in *Counting and Comparing*. In that unit, students had many opportunities to develop their sense of numbers and quantities, to count and compare amounts, and to measure objects by comparing them directly.

This unit focuses on 5 Mathematical Emphases:

1 Linear Measurement Understanding length and using linear units

Math Focus Points

◆ Understanding what length is

◆ Identifying the longest dimension of an object

◆ Comparing lengths of different objects

◆ Repeating multiple nonstandard units to quantify length

◆ Developing strategies for measuring the length of an object

In *Counting and Comparing,* students approached measurement through direct comparison: "Is my pencil longer or shorter than a tower of 10 cubes?" In this unit, students use multiple nonstandard units, such as craft sticks or cubes to quantify length: "How many craft sticks long is this desk? The path from the window to the door?" or "How many cubes long is my shoe? This pencil?" As they measure lengths around their classroom, students grapple with important ideas in measurement, such as how to line up units (or tools) with the object being measured, and what happens if those units are (or are not) laid straight or if there are (or are not) gaps or overlaps between them. Measuring with units is a complicated idea that develops gradually. Students need many opportunities over the course of the elementary years to make sense of the idea that one unit can be repeated to describe a length and to develop strategies for doing so accurately.

2 Counting and Quantity Developing strategies for accurately counting a set of objects by ones

Math Focus Points

◆ Counting a set of objects and creating an equivalent set

◆ Connecting number words, numerals, and quantities

◆ Keeping track of a growing set of objects

◆ Counting spaces and moving on a gameboard

◆ Creating a set of a given size

◆ Developing and analyzing visual images for quantities up to 10

In this unit, students continue to count in a variety of contexts. For example, the measurement activities provide important and meaningful contexts for counting and keeping track of amounts. In order for five- and six-year-olds to figure out how long an object or length is, they must count how many units—cubes or crafts sticks—fit along one dimension.

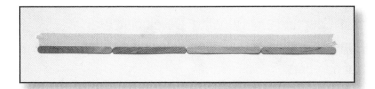

Activities such as *Grab and Count: Two Handfuls, Collect 15 Together,* and the Counting Jar provide experience counting larger amounts, up to 15 or so. Students who can accurately count ten objects may have to revisit various counting skills as the numbers of items they are asked to count increase. For example, they need to learn the names and sequence of the numbers over 10 and what the written numerals for those numbers look like. They may need to refine their strategies for keeping track of a count as the number of items grows.

This unit also uses the ideas and skills of counting to build a foundation on which students will develop an understanding of the operation of addition. Many games and activities ask students to count a set of objects, add a small amount, and then ask, "Now how many?" As students keep track of the total number of objects in growing collections, they must count accurately and develop strategies for organizing and keeping track. But they are also encouraged to begin combining small amounts rather than counting whole collections starting from one each time.

3 Whole Number Operations Making sense of and developing strategies to solve addition and subtraction problems with small numbers

Math Focus Points

◈ Finding the total after a small amount (1, 2, 3) is added to a set of up to 7

◈ Combining two amounts

◈ Modeling the action of combining and separating situations

◈ Separating one amount from another

◈ Adding or subtracting one to/from numbers up to 10

◈ Adding to or subtracting from one quantity to make another quantity

◈ Decomposing numbers in different ways

◈ Exploring combinations of a number (e.g., 6 is 3 and 3 and also 5 and 1)

In this unit, students are introduced to addition and subtraction through story problems about combining and separating. When students solve story problems, they first need to make sense of the situation: What sequence of actions is being described in the problem? What does each amount represent? Is the second amount to be *combined with* the first, or is it to be *separated from* the first? Will the result be more or less than the initial amount? To help them answer such questions, students retell the stories, act them out, and solve them by modeling the action involved.

As kindergarteners become proficient with counting small quantities, they can begin to explore combinations of these quantities. In this unit, students find many ways to arrange sets of square tiles for the numbers 5–10. They also repeatedly toss a set of two-color counters and record the way they land (e.g., 3 are red and 3 are yellow). As they do this work, they find that there are different ways to make a number—6 is 3 and 3 and also 5 and 1.

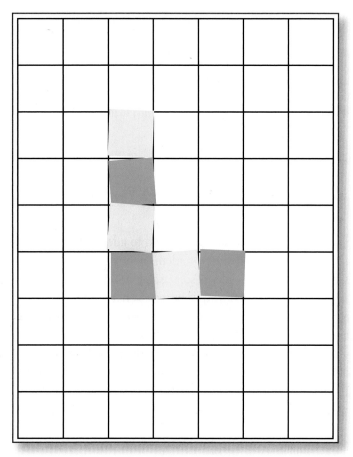

Although the contexts of the story problems and activities presented in this unit can be modeled by the operation of addition or subtraction, kindergarteners may not yet see them as such; that is, they may see them as contexts that involve counting, rather than an action such as combining or separating. Also, they may not see that different contexts involve the same math ideas. For example, students who play *One More, One Fewer* fluently may not quickly and easily solve a story problem about adding (or subtracting) one. Students need many opportunities to count, to visualize and model the action of different types of problems, and to discuss the ways they are similar and different in order to develop an understanding of the operations of addition and subtraction and to be able to use efficient strategies across problem types.

4 Counting and Quantity Developing an understanding of the magnitude and position of numbers

Math Focus Points

◆ Developing an understanding of more than and fewer than

◆ Comparing two quantities to determine which is more

Students continue to develop an understanding of more and fewer as they count and compare quantities, visualize the action of combining and separating situations, and think about whether the result will be more or fewer. They play games that involve finding the total after 1 has been added or taken away. For some students, these activities connect to the work they are doing with counting and learning the sequence of numbers: "I know that 6 is 1 more than 5 because 6 is the number that comes after 5." Others are developing an image of the quantities that the counting sequence represent and a sense of how those quantities are related. For example, they may see 5 as *2 and 2 and 1* or think of 7 as more than 5 and less than 10 or solve a problem about adding one more thus: "If you have 5 [holding up 1 hand] and get 1 more [holding up 1 finger on the other hand] you have 6." When these students play *Build It/Change It,* they may know that they need 2 more to make 5 into 7 or may reason about the quantities as they play *Double Compare:* "Kaitlyn has 2 and 3; Jennifer has 4 and 5. Both of Jennifer's numbers are bigger than both of Kaitlyn's numbers, so Jennifer has more."

5 Whole Number Operations **Using manipulatives, drawings, tools, and notation to show strategies and solutions**

Math Focus Points

◆ Recording measurements with pictures, numbers, and/or words

◆ Using numbers to represent quantities and to record how many

◆ Using a Ten-Frame to develop visual images of quantities up to 10

◆ Recording an arrangement of a quantity

Throughout this unit and the *Investigations* curriculum, students use mathematical tools and representations to model and solve problems and to clarify and communicate their thinking. For example, students develop images of the numbers up to 10 by arranging square tiles and working on a Ten-Frame; they use pictures, numbers, and/or words to record measurements; and they have several opportunities to use numbers to represent quantities. (The calendar and number line offer models of the written numbers, in sequence, for students to use as reference.) When students are asked to represent mathematical work on paper, they are encouraged to do so in ways that make sense to them. As they develop ways to record, and as they have opportunities to interpret what others have recorded, they learn how to communicate mathematical information.

This Unit also focuses on

◆ Thinking strategically about moves on a gameboard

Classroom Routines focus on

◆ Using the calendar as a tool for keeping track of time

◆ Developing strategies for counting accurately

◆ Considering whether order matters when you count

◆ Comparing quantities

◆ Collecting, counting, representing, describing, and comparing data

◆ Determining what comes next in a repeating pattern

◆ Describing repeating patterns

LOOKING FORWARD The work in this unit will be built on throughout the rest of Kindergarten, and particularly in *How Many Do You Have?* In that unit, students extend their work with measurement and encounter a variety of situations that involve counting, combining, and comparing amounts to 20. They revisit story problems, with a continued focus on making sense of the action of the problems, and work to model and record solutions. Finally, the work students did in this unit with making numbers in different ways will be extended as they focus on generating multiple combinations of a number and recording their work.

Assessment

IN THIS UNIT

Every session in this unit provides an opportunity for Ongoing Assessment. In addition, assessment checklists are provided to keep track of your observations about students' work with concepts and ideas that are benchmarks for this unit.

ONGOING ASSESSMENT: Observing Students at Work

The following sessions provide **Ongoing Assessment: Observing Students at Work** opportunities:

- **Session 1.1, p. 30**
- **Session 1.2, p. 36**
- **Session 1.3, pp. 41–42**
- **Session 1.5, p. 50**
- **Session 2.1, pp. 61 and 62**
- **Session 2.2, p. 68**

- **Session 2.3, p. 74**
- **Session 2.4, p. 78**
- **Session 2.5, p. 83**
- **Session 3.1, p. 93**
- **Session 3.3, p. 102**
- **Session 3.4, p. 106**

- **Session 3.6, p. 115**
- **Session 4.1, pp. 131–132**
- **Session 4.3, pp. 140–141**
- **Session 4.4, p. 145**
- **Session 4.5, p. 151**
- **Session 4.7, p. 160**

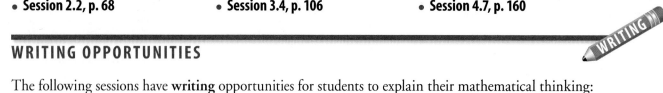

WRITING OPPORTUNITIES

The following sessions have **writing** opportunities for students to explain their mathematical thinking:

- **Session 1.2, p. 35**
  Student Activity Book, p. 26

- **Session 1.5, p. 49**
  Student Activity Book, p. 28

- **Session 2.1, p. 60**
  Student Activity Book, p. 31

- **Session 2.4, p. 77**
  Student Activity Book, p. 33

- **Session 4.7, p. 160**
  Student Activity Book, p. 40

PORTFOLIO OPPORTUNITIES

The following sessions have work appropriate for a **portfolio:**

- **Sessions 1.2, 2.5, 3.3, 4.6,
  pp. 36, 80–84, 100–103, 153–156**
  Counting Jar Activity

- **Sessions 2.4–3.4, pp. 76–108**
  Student Activity Book, p. 33

- **Sessions 4.7–4.9, pp. 157–167**
  Student Activity Book, p. 40

Assessing the Benchmarks

Observing students as they engage in conversation about their ideas is a primary means to assess their mathematical understanding. Consider all of your students' work, not just the written assessments. See the chart below for suggestions about key activities to observe.

An Assessment Checklist for keeping track of how students line up multiple units to measure length is introduced in Session 1.1. A second Assessment Checklist is introduced in Session 2.1 to keep track of students' growing counting skills. A third Assessment Checklist is introduced in Session 3.3 to keep track of how students determine what is one more or one fewer than a given number. Use these checklists to determine which students need to complete an End-of-Unit Assessment interview. Over the course of Sessions 4.8 and 4.9, meet individually with students who have not yet clearly met each benchmark or about whom you have questions.

 Checklist Available

Benchmarks in This Unit	Key Activities to Observe	Assessment
1. Measure the length of an object by lining up multiple units.	**Sessions 1.1–1.4:** Measuring Shoes **Sessions 1.3–1.5:** Measuring with Sticks **Sessions 1.5 and 2.1–2.3:** Measuring with Cubes	**Session 1.1:** Assessment Checklist: Measuring Lengths ✓
2. Count a set of up to 15 objects.	**Sessions 2.1–2.3:** *Grab and Count: Two Handfuls* **Sessions 2.5 and 3.2–3.5:** *Collect 15 Together* **Sessions 2.5 and 3.2–3.3:** Counting Jar	**Session 2.1:** Assessment Checklist: Counting ✓
3. Figure out what is one more or one fewer than a number.	**Sessions 3.3–3.7:** *One More, One Fewer* **Sessions 4.2–4.6:** Counting Jar	**Session 3.3:** Assessment Checklist: One More, One Fewer ✓

Relating the Mathematical Emphases to the Benchmarks

Mathematical Emphases	Benchmarks
Linear Measurement Understanding length and using linear units	1
Counting and Quantity Developing strategies for accurately counting a set of objects by ones	2
Whole Number Operations Making sense of and developing strategies to solve addition and subtraction problems with small numbers	3
Counting and Quantity Developing an understanding of the magnitude and position of numbers	3
Whole Number Operations Using manipulatives, drawings, tools, and notation to show strategies and solutions	

Algebra Connections

IN THIS UNIT

This unit provides opportunities for students to engage with ideas that lay a foundation for algebra. Five- and six-year-olds can and do think algebraically. Part of the work of Kindergarten is helping students learn to verbalize those thoughts, both as a way to engage with generalizations about numbers and operations and as a foundation for meaningful use of algebraic notation in the future.

Kindergarten students will work on the idea of equivalence many times over the course of the year. Understanding equivalence involves recognizing that a number describes the size of a set. The number of objects in a set is fixed no matter how it is arranged and counted, and different sets may have the same number of objects. Explorations of these issues offer opportunities for algebraic discussions.

In *Counting and Comparing,* students discussed whether changing the order in which a set of objects is counted changes the total. For example, in Unit 2, students counted the total of five red rods and three yellow rods, and concluded that it did not matter whether they counted the red rods first, and then the yellow, or if they began with the yellow; either way, they got eight. They further asserted that this was not special about rods, nor was it special about the number 8. Their observations about the constancy of the total, no matter what the order of counting a set of objects, lays the foundation for what they will later call the commutative property of addition: For any numbers a and b, $a + b = b + a$.

Given this background, consider the following vignette from Ms. Epstein's Kindergarten class. Students have been tossing 6 two-color counters to see how many land showing yellow, and how many land showing red, and are now gathered to share their findings.

Dennis: I have three reds and three yellows.

Mary: I have two reds and four yellows.

Abby: I have the opposite.

Teacher: What do you mean by opposite?

Abby: Mary had two reds and four yellows, and I have two yellows and four reds. It's the opposite.

The children in this class are identifying different ways to decompose six objects into two parts. Thus, a set of three red chips and three yellows is equivalent to two reds and four yellows which, in turn, is equivalent to two yellows and four reds. The different sets are equivalent because they all have the same number of objects.

Furthermore, Abby notices that there is something the same about Mary's two reds and four yellows and her own two yellows and four reds. Even though Mary has more yellows and Abby has more reds, both arrangements separate the set into one part with four objects, the other with two. She has named this feature "opposite."

The discussion in Ms. Epstein's class continues:

Kiyo: I have five reds and one yellow.

Lionel: I have one red and five yellows.

Hugo: It's opposite again.

Teacher: What is opposite? What do you mean?

Hugo: Kiyo has five reds and one yellow; Lionel has one red and five yellows. It's the opposite.

Lionel: It's five, one and one, then five. It's opposite.

Carmen: And look! There's six reds and zero yellows, and six yellows and zero reds!

Teacher: This is an important thing to notice. I wonder whether we will see opposites when we play *Toss the Chips* again?

Again, the students are discussing an idea that they will later represent as the commutative property of addition: $a + b = b + a$. Yet, they are engaged by this discussion and are excited by their observations. It seems that this is the first time they have encountered this principle. They asserted with such assurance that you could count red and then yellow or yellow and then red and still get the same total. What happened to that understanding?

In fact, most likely these students have not forgotten that idea and would make the same assertions with assurance. Today they behave as though they have encountered the idea for the first time, because they have! Although, from an adult perspective, it may seem they are working on the *same* idea—that you can change the order of addends without changing the result—to a kindergartener, the two contexts seem very different.

Rather than counting a set of objects of two different colors to find the total, the class is finding different ways to decompose a set into two groups. They notice that if you toss six chips and get x yellows and y reds, then it is also possible to get y yellows and x reds. *Both* of these contexts contribute to students' developing understanding of numerical relationships.

Today students are talking about specific numbers: e.g., six chips can be four reds and two yellows or two reds and four yellows. Once the students have named their observation "opposites," the teacher alerts them to the possibility of noticing opposites again when they play the game with another number of chips. Indeed on another day, when they play *Toss the Chips* with seven chips, Ms. Epstein finds the opportunity to ask whether this property holds more generally.

Emma: Look! Mitchell got three reds and four yellows, and I got four reds and three yellows. It's opposites.

Teacher: Are there any more opposites for seven?

Kiyo: There's 6 reds and 1 yellow, and 1 yellow and 6 reds.

Lionel: Hugo got 5 reds and 2 yellows. So 2 reds and 5 yellows works, too.

Teacher: We saw opposites when we tossed six chips and now again when we toss seven chips. Do you think this is special about the numbers 6 and 7? Or do you think it will happen with other numbers, too?

Although these students are not yet explicitly thinking in terms of addition, activities such as *Toss the Chips* allow them to become familiar with significant numerical relationships: six can be a group of five and another of one; seven can be a group of four and a group of three. Furthermore, the same number can be decomposed in different ways: a group of four and a group of three is equivalent to a group of five and a group of two.

As students come to recognize that these numerical relationships remain constant across different contexts, they develop an understanding of the operation of addition. That is, what had once been very different actions—e.g., counting a set of objects of two colors and separating a set into two groups—are all subsumed under one operation.

In *Measuring and Counting,* students may discover that the same numerical relationships hold when they work on story problems, make arrangements of tiles, or play *Racing Bears.* Although for now, students' observations of regularities among numbers may be confined to particular contexts, as they notice the same regularities across contexts, they begin to make observations about the operation of addition.

Even though at this time the students' level of abstraction is limited, these examples illustrate the kind of "early algebraic reasoning" that is accessible to kindergarteners. This early algebra work involves students in reasoning, generalizing, representing, and communicating. They explore questions that may begin with a particular problem—six chips may be composed of four reds and two yellows and also of two reds and four yellows—but extend to a *whole class* of problems. Any number of chips can be decomposed in different ways, and for any decomposition, the parts can be switched to form its "opposite," another way of decomposing the same number.

Note: In the text for the sessions, you will find flags that identify where these early algebra discussions are likely to arise. Some of the **Teacher Notes** and **Dialogue Boxes** further elaborate the ideas and illustrate students' conversations about them.

Classroom Routines

Classroom Routines offer practice and review of key concepts for this grade level. These daily activities, to be done in 10 minutes outside of math class, occur in a regular rotation every 4–5 days. Specific directions for the day's routine are provided in each session. For the full description and variations of each classroom routine, see *Implementing Investigations in Kindergarten.*

Calendar

Students continue to review the numbers and counting sequence to 31 and the names and sequence of the days of the week. Students also use the calendar to determine how many days until (or since) a special event and explain their strategies.

Math Focus Points

- Using the calendar as a tool for keeping track of time
- Developing strategies for counting accurately

Attendance

Students continue to count to determine the total number of students present and to explore what happens when the count begins with different students. In order to help students connect the counting numbers to the quantities they represent, the class discusses how many students have counted, midway through the count. Students also compare two groups, determine which group has more, and determine how many more are in this larger group.

Math Focus Points

- Developing strategies for counting accurately
- Considering whether order matters when you count
- Comparing quantities

Today's Question

Students record their response to a survey question with two possible answers on a two-column table. Class discussion focuses on describing and interpreting the data.

Math Focus Points

- Collecting, counting, representing, describing, and comparing data

Patterns on the Pocket Chart

Students see part of a repeating pattern. They describe and extend the pattern, determining what would come next if the pattern were to continue.

Math Focus Points

- Determining what comes next in a repeating pattern
- Describing repeating patterns

Practice and Review

Practice and review play a critical role in the *Investigations* program. The following components and features are available to provide regular reinforcement of key mathematical concepts and procedures.

Books	Features	In This Unit . . .
Curriculum Unit	**Classroom Routines** offer practice and review of key concepts for this grade level. These daily activities, to be done in ten minutes outside of math class, occur in a regular rotation every 4–5 days. Specific directions for the day's routine are provided in each session. For the full description and variations of each classroom routine see *Implementing Investigations in Kindergarten*.	• **All sessions**
Student Activity Book	**Practice** pages in the *Student Activity Book* provide one of two types of written practice: **reinforcement** of the content of the unit or **enrichment** opportunities.	• **Session 1.5** • **Session 2.3** • **Session 3.4** • **Session 4.1** • **Session 4.8**
	Homework pages in the *Student Activity Book* are an extension of the work done in class. At times they help students prepare for upcoming activities.	• **Session 1.2**
Student Math Handbook Flip Chart	**Math Words and Ideas** in the *Student Math Handbook Flip Chart* are pages that summarize key words and ideas. Most Words and Ideas pages have at least one exercise.	• **Student Math Handbook Flip Chart, pp. 11–14, 18–22, 25–31, 36–38**

Supporting the Range of Learners

Sessions	1.1	1.2	1.3	1.4	1.5	2.1	2.2	2.3	2.4	2.5	3.1	3.2	3.3	3.4	3.5	4.1	4.3	4.4	4.5	4.6	4.7	4.8
Intervention	•	•	•		•	•	•	•	•	•	•		•	•		•	•		•		•	
Extension			•	•		•	•		•	•		•		•	•			•		•		
ELL	•	•										•										•

Intervention

Suggestions are made to support and engage students who are having difficulty with a particular idea, activity, or problem.

Extension

Suggestions are made to support and engage students who finish early or may be ready for additional challenge.

English Language Learners (ELL)

As English Language Learners work through the material in *Measuring and Counting,* they need continued practice with the relevant vocabulary in the context of meaningful activities. You can model the use of math-related vocabulary by thinking aloud as you engage in various activities. You can also ask students questions as they work.

The language structure "How many . . . ?" is essential to many of the activities in this unit. English Language Learners will acquire the language through repeated modeling and practice of the language structure. You can also model the meanings of math-related words such as *more* and *fewer* in context.

You can demonstrate superlatives (*long/longer/longest; short/shorter/shortest*) in much the same way you demonstrated comparatives in *Counting and Comparing.* Begin by showing students the pair of different-sized circles from the *Counting and Comparing* exercise. Then show a third, even larger circle. Have students work in pairs and with other sets of shapes or numbers, encouraging them to use superlatives as they ask each other questions about the sets.

Working with the Range of Learners: Classroom Cases is a set of episodes written by teachers that focuses on meeting the needs of the range of learners in the classroom. In the first section, *Setting up the Mathematical Community,* teachers write about how they create a supportive and productive learning environment in their classrooms. In the next section, *Accommodations for Learning,* teachers focus on specific modifications they make to meet the needs of some of their learners. In the last section, *Language and Representation,* teachers share how they help students use representations and develop language to investigate and express mathematical ideas. The questions at the end of each case provide a starting point for your own reflection or for discussion with colleagues. See *Implementing Investigations in Kindergarten* for this set of episodes.

Mathematical Emphases

Linear Measurement Understanding length and using linear units

Math Focus Points

◆ Understanding what length is

◆ Identifying the longest dimension of an object

◆ Comparing lengths of different objects

◆ Repeating multiple nonstandard units to quantify length

◆ Developing strategies for measuring the length of an object

Counting and Quantity Developing strategies for accurately counting a set of objects by ones

Math Focus Points

◆ Counting a set of objects and creating an equivalent set

Whole Number Operations Using manipulatives, drawings, tools, and notation to show strategies and solutions

Math Focus Points

◆ Recording measurements with pictures, numbers, and/or words

Measuring and Counting

	Student Activity Book	Student Math Handbook Flip Chart	Professional Development: Read Ahead of Time	
SESSION 1.1 p. 28				
Measuring Our Shoes Students discuss length and how to determine how long something is. They use cubes to measure the length of their shoes and discuss the strategies they used for measuring.			• **Mathematics in This Unit,** p. 12 • **Teacher Note:** Learning About Length: Lining Up Units, p. 169	
SESSION 1.2 p. 33				
Measuring Different Shoe Lengths Students use cubes to measure the length of a variety of shoes, using outlines created by the teacher and their classmates.	26	36, 38		
SESSION 1.3 p. 38				
Measuring with Sticks Students discuss how they could use craft sticks to measure the length of a strip of ribbon or tape on the classroom floor. During Math Workshop they use craft sticks to measure the length of various strips and cubes to measure the length of shoes.	27	36, 38		
SESSION 1.4 p. 45				
Comparing Lengths of Shoes Students continue to use craft sticks and cubes to measure the length of objects. Class discussion focuses on which shoes were the longest and shortest and why there may be different measurements for the same shoe.	26	36, 38		

Classroom Routines See page 20 for an overview.

Attendance	Patterns on the Pocket Chart
• No materials needed	• Pocket Chart or Sentence Pocket Chart
Calendar	• M7, Question Mark Cards, Cut apart and store.
• Monthly calendar or class pocket calendar	• M6, Arrow Cards for the Pocket Chart, Cut apart
Today's Question	and store.
• Today's Question chart for Session 1.3	
See instructions on page 38.	

Materials to Gather

- **A book about shoes such as** *Shoes, Shoes, Shoes* **by Ann Morris;** *Shoes* **by Elizabeth Winthrop;** *New Shoes for Sylvia* **by Johanna Hurwitz;** *Shoes Like Miss Alice's* **by Angela Johnson; or** *A Pair of Red Clogs* **by Masako Matsuno** (optional)
- **Connecting cubes** (20 per student)

- **Connecting Cubes**
- **Pencils, pens, or markers**
- **Materials for the Counting Jar routine** (as you have set it up)

- **Craft sticks** (10–12 per pair of students)
- **Students' completed shoe outlines**
- **Materials for Tracing Your Shoe** See Session 1.2.
- **Materials for Measuring Shoes** See Session 1.2.
- **Materials for Counting Jar** See Session 1.2.

- **Alternative non-standard measuring tools that are a bit longer** (unsharpened pencils, long straws) or a bit shorter (new crayons, short straws) than craft sticks (optional for the variation)
- **Materials for Measuring with Sticks** See Session 1.3.
- **Materials for Measuring Shoes** See Session 1.2.
- **Materials for Counting Jar** See Session 1.2.

Materials to Prepare

- **M3, Assessment Checklist: Measuring Lengths** ☑ **Make copies.** (3–4 per class, plus extras as needed)
- **M1–M2, Family Letter** Make copies. (1 per student)

- **Counting Jar** Place 11 craft sticks in the jar.
- **M4, Measuring Shoes** Make copies. (as needed)
- **Traced edges of at least 4 shoes** Choose people who are important to your students (e.g., the principal, the art teacher, the gym teacher) and include a range of shoes sizes (e.g., adult men and women, children who are older and younger than your students). Label each tracing with the name of the person (Sr. Ruiz's shoe, Ms. Bond's sneaker, Mrs. Barzey's baby, Audrey). Place the shoe outlines in a basket or bin at the Measuring Shoes activity.

- **Strips of wide ribbon (or adding machine, masking, or colored electric tape)** Cut a strip that it is exactly as long as five craft sticks laid end to end and label it A. Make another strip that is three and a half craft sticks long and label it B. Tape these strips down where students can gather around them.
- **Strips the length of classroom items** Cut, label, and tape additional strips along the length of about 10 different classroom items that are between one and four feet long (such as the seat of a chair, a table top, and a window sill).
- **Paths** Cut, label with letters, and tape additional strips to the floor to create several straight paths of no more than 4 feet (such as from the door to the science table). Create an answer key that tells how many craft sticks long each strip is.
- **M5, Measuring with Sticks** Make copies. (as needed)

☑ Checklist Available

Measuring and Counting,
continued

SESSION 1.5 p. 48	Student Activity Book	Student Math Handbook Flip Chart	Professional Development: Read Ahead of Time	
Measuring with Cubes During Math Workshop, students use cubes to measure a variety of objects and continue to measure strips with craft sticks. Class discussion focuses on strategies for measuring and why there may be different measurements for the same strip.	28–29		• **Teacher Notes:** Counting Is More Than 1, 2, 3, p. 170; Observing Kindergarteners as They Count, p. 171 • **Dialogue Box:** Measuring with Sticks, p. 181	

Materials to Gather	Materials to Prepare
• **Connecting cubes** • **Craft sticks** • **Materials for Measuring With Sticks** See Session 1.3. • **Materials for Counting Jar** See Session 1.2.	• **M8, Measuring with Cubes** Make copies. (as needed) • **Two to three Measurement Collections** Collect 10 objects, each 2 to 15 inches long. Include some objects that are different from those used in *Counting and Comparing*. Include some for which measuring length will be fairly straightforward (flat objects such as boxes, envelopes, or books) and others that may present a challenge (objects with rounder or less regular shapes, such as paper cups, paper tubes, or plastic bottles). Label each object with its identifying double letters (i.e., AA, BB) to distinguish it from the strips of tape. Put each collection in a bin or box. You may want to make yourself an answer key for these objects so that you know what object is labeled with what letter.

Measuring Our Shoes

Math Focus Points

- Understanding what length is
- Identifying the longest dimension of an object
- Repeating multiple nonstandard units to quantify length
- Developing strategies for measuring the length of an object

Vocabulary

long
length
measure

Today's Plan		Materials
ACTIVITY ❶ **Introducing Measuring Shoes**	5–10 MIN CLASS	• A book about shoes
ACTIVITY ❷ **How Long Is Your Shoe?**	15–25 MIN INDIVIDUALS	• M3* ☑ • Connecting cubes
DISCUSSION ❸ **How Did You Measure?**	10 MIN CLASS	• Connecting cubes
SESSION FOLLOW-UP ❹ **Homework**		• M1–M2, Family Letter*

*See *Materials to Prepare,* p. 25.

Classroom Routines

Attendance: How Many Have Counted? Count around the circle as usual but pause several times during the count to ask students how many people have counted so far and how they know. Help students see why the number they say represents the number of students who have counted so far and that the last number represents the total number of students in class today.

ACTIVITY

Introducing Measuring Shoes

5–10 MIN   CLASS

Begin this unit by telling or reading a story about shoes. ❶ ❷

Delilah Lampert went shopping one day and bought a pair of shoes for herself. They were very colorful: purple and yellow and green! After she wore them a few times she suddenly thought, "I think my cousin Lorena would really like these. I should give them to her." So she called her cousin, who lived far away, on the phone. Her cousin liked the idea of purple and yellow and green shoes, but she wasn't sure they would fit. "I don't know, Delilah," she said, "I wear pretty small shoes. I think they may be too big for me." How could Delilah and Lorena figure out how long their shoes are?

After you finish telling the story, discuss the length of a shoe.

Shoes come in all different sizes. I wear a different size shoe than you do, and a baby just learning to walk wears another size shoe. What if we wanted to figure out how long our shoes are? What's the length of my shoe? If I ask how long my shoe is, where would I measure? ❸

Students might say:

"Along the side of your shoe."

"From the back to the front."

"We can measure the bottom of the shoe to see how long it is."

Some may not have ideas about how to measure how long something is, and others may be unfamiliar with the word *length*. ❹

Today you are going to measure the length of your own shoe the way they do in shoe stores: from heel [point to the heel of your shoe] to toe [point to the toe of your shoe]. You are going to keep your shoes on and find a way to use cubes to measure your shoe.

ACTIVITY

② How Long Is Your Shoe?

15–25 MIN   INDIVIDUALS

Students decide for themselves how to use cubes to measure the length of their shoe. They do so with their shoes on.

ONGOING ASSESSMENT: Observing Students at Work

Students repeat nonstandard units (cubes) to measure the length of an object (a shoe).

- **How do students use cubes to measure the length of the shoe?**
  Do they place them singly or link them together? Are there gaps or overlaps? Do they line up the first cube with the edge of their shoe? Do they make a straight line?

As you circulate, take note of students who use different strategies to measure their shoe, to inform the discussion at the end of this session.⑤

Assessment Checklist: Measuring Lengths

Student	Measures the length of the object	Lines up units the length of the object	Accurately counts the number of units used	Notes
Jennifer	✓ shoe—heel to toe	✓ snaps cubes together and lines up next to shoe	✓	
Lionel	✓ tape	✓ makes a line of stick on tape but leaves gaps	✓	
Cindy	No covers shoe outline with cubes		✓	
Carmen	✓	puts cubes in line along curve of shoe outline	✓	
Brad	✓	✓ line of cubes across big book —next to each other but not connected	No 13 cubes missed #11	

DIFFERENTIATION: Supporting the Range of Learners

Intervention Some students lay cubes separately alongside their shoe, perhaps with spaces or overlaps between cubes. It is important that students try their own ways of measuring, particularly because they are just developing a sense of length and what it means to measure.❻ Such strategies will be discussed in the conversations at the end of this session and Session 1.5.

DISCUSSION

3 How Did You Measure?

10 MIN   CLASS

Math Focus Points for Discussion

◆ Developing strategies for measuring the length of an object

Begin the discussion by asking students to share their measurements. Then, ask them to share the strategies they used to measure their shoes.

How did you use the cubes to measure how long your shoe is?

Ask students who used different methods to explain their strategy in words and to demonstrate it with cubes.

Students demonstrate the strategies they used to measure their shoes.

Ask the class to comment on and compare the different methods students used.

Professional Development

❻ **Teacher Note:** Learning About Length: Lining Up Units, p. 169

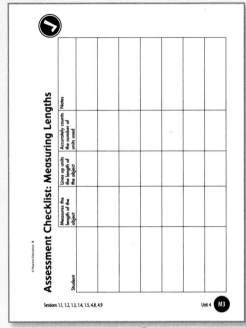

▲ **Resource Masters, M3** ✓

Math Note

⑦ Understanding Length Because kindergarteners are just beginning to make sense of what length is and how to describe how long something is, they will need many opportunities to measure different lengths with same-sized objects in order to make sense of the conventions of measuring.

I noticed that some people snapped the cubes together and other people left some space between the cubes as they lined them up. Do you think that makes a difference? Why or why not?

I noticed that sometimes people put the first cube in line with the end of the shoe and sometimes the first cube was not even with the end of the shoe. Do you think that matters? Why or why not?

I noticed that some people followed the curve of their shoe and some people put the cubes in a straight line. Do you think that makes a difference? Why or why not?

Asking students to consider these differences helps them begin to understand how to measure and what is important to pay attention to as they measure.⑦

SESSION FOLLOW-UP

4 Homework

Family Letter: Send home a copy of Family Letter (M1–M2).

Measuring Different Shoe Lengths

Math Focus Points

◆ Repeating multiple nonstandard units to quantify length

◆ Developing strategies for measuring the length of an object

◆ Recording measurements with pictures, numbers, and/or words

◆ Counting a set of objects and creating an equivalent set

Vocabulary

longest

shortest

Today's Plan		Materials
ACTIVITY **① Introducing Math Workshop Activities**	5–10 MIN CLASS	• M4* • Prepared shoe outlines*; connecting cubes; Counting Jar*
MATH WORKSHOP **② Tracing and Measuring Shoes and Counting Sticks** ② Tracing Your Shoe ② Measuring Shoes ② Counting Jar	20–30 MIN	**2A** • Pencils, pens, or markers **2B** • *Student Activity Book,* p. 26 • M4* • Connecting cubes; prepared shoe outlines*; students' shoe outlines **2C** • Counting Jar*; materials for the Counting Jar (as you have set it up)
DISCUSSION **③ Checking In**	5 MIN CLASS	
SESSION FOLLOW-UP **④ Practice and Homework**		• *Student Math Handbook Flip Chart,* pp. 36, 38

*See *Materials to Prepare,* p. 25.

Classroom Routines

Calendar: Days of the Week Use the calendar to review the days of the week, noting which days are school days and which are weekend (or non school) days.

Differentiation

❶ English Language Learners In *Counting and Comparing,* English Language Learners learned about comparatives such as *longer* and *shorter.* In this session, they will also need to understand superlatives such as *longest* and *shortest.* You can work with a small group of English Language Learners on the Measuring Shoes activity during Math Workshop. Arrange the shoes in order of size to demonstrate vocabulary such as *short/shorter/ shortest* and *long/longer/longest.* Which shoe is *shorter,* this one or that one? Which shoe is *shortest* of these three? Can you find a shoe that is *longer* than this one? Which shoe is the *longest* of all? Students can practice the vocabulary by lining up groups of shoes and asking one another similar questions about them.

ACTIVITY
1 Introducing Math Workshop Activities

5–10 MIN   CLASS

Show students the set of shoe outlines you prepared ahead of time. In the next few days, you are going to measure many people's shoes— people who are in our class and people who are not in our class. You will find out how long different people's shoes are by measuring the length of shoes that have been traced on paper. I traced the shoes of some people who are not in our class. Which shoe do you think is the **longest**? The **shortest**?❶ Why do you think so?

Choose one of the smaller shoe outlines.

If I wanted to use cubes to measure the length [point out the length] of this shoe outline, what could I do? Remember that we're measuring from the heel to the toe.

Students might say:

"Make a line of cubes that goes from the heel to the toe."

Could you show us, [Beth]? [Hugo], can you count how many cubes [Beth] used? Does everyone agree that [Beth] used [8] cubes?

After you figure out how long the shoe is, you write it on your recording sheet. [Beth] would write [Cindy] here [point to line on Measuring Shoes (M4)] because she measured [Cindy]'s shoe.

Now, [Beth] needs to find a way to show what she found out about [Cindy]'s shoe. What could [Beth] write or draw to show what she found out?

Demonstrate students' suggestions for recording the length of the shoe, which are likely to include writing the number 8, drawing eight cubes, and drawing a picture of how the cubes lined up on the outline.

One of the activities during Math Workshop today will be measuring these shoe outlines. Another activity will be making a tracing of your shoe, while it's on your foot, to add to the [basket] of shoes to measure.

Ask a student volunteer to help you demonstrate how partners can work together to make an outline of both of your shoes. Explain that each person needs to label their shoe outline with their name and place it in the basket of shoes to be measured.

Finally, show students the Counting Jar with 11 craft sticks in it, and explain that this will be the third Math Workshop activity.

MATH WORKSHOP

20–30 MIN

② Tracing and Measuring Shoes and Counting Sticks

Explain that the following three activities, one of which is the Counting Jar, are available during this Math Workshop. Remind students what each activity entails, what materials are required, and where they are located.

②A Tracing Your Shoe

PAIRS

Partners work together to trace each other's shoes. They label the outline with their name and add it to the basket at the Measuring Shoes activity.

Students trace the outlines of one another's shoe onto paper.

②B Measuring Shoes

INDIVIDUALS

Students choose a shoe outline and use cubes to measure how long it is. They record their findings on *Student Activity Book* page 26.

Teaching Note

② **Keep Your Shoe On!** Ask students to keep their shoes on as they trace them.

Name _____ Date _____
Measuring and Counting

Measuring Shoes 🖊

1. I measured _____'s shoe.
   This is how long it was:

2. I measured _____'s shoe.
   This is how long it was:

3. I measured _____'s shoe.
   This is how long it was:

26 Unit 4   Session 1.2

▲ **Student Activity Book, p. 26; Resource Masters, M4**

❸ **Assembling a Portfolio** Because students do Counting Jar in every unit, it provides an opportunity to see students' growth over time. For one of the Counting Jars in this unit, have students record their work on a piece of paper you can collect and put in their portfolio.

ONGOING ASSESSMENT: Observing Students at Work

Students repeat a nonstandard unit (cubes) to measure the length of a variety of sizes of the same type of object (a shoe).

- **Do students measure the length of the shoe outline?** Do they measure something else (e.g., the length of the paper or the width, perimeter, or area of the outline)?

- **How do students use cubes to measure the shoe outline?** Do they place the first cube at the edge of the shoe outline? Do they make a straight line from heel to toe? Do they link the cubes together or leave them separate? Are there gaps or overlaps between the cubes?

- **How do students count and keep track of the number of cubes?**

- **How do students record their measurements?** Do they use pictures? Numbers? Words? Some combination of these?

DIFFERENTIATION: Supporting the Range of Learners

Intervention Some students measure the area, perimeter, or width of the outline or the length of the paper. Remind these students about the conversation you had about the length of shoes. Ask them what the longest part of the shoe is. If they are unsure, remind them that the class agreed to measure from heel to toe, and ask how they can measure that distance.

2C Counting Jar

INDIVIDUALS

Students count the objects in the Counting Jar. They make a set of the same size and record what they found out.❸

ONGOING ASSESSMENT: Observing Students at Work

Students count a set of objects, create an equivalent set, and record their work.

- **How do students count the objects in the jar?** Do they organize the objects in any way? Do they know the sequence of number names? Do they count each item once and only once? Do they double-check?

- **How do students create an equivalent set?** Do they think, "The Counting Jar had 11 craft sticks so I need 11 [tiles]. 1, 2, 3 . . ."? Do they recreate the Counting Jar set, matching them one to one? Do they double-check?

- **How do students record their work?** Do they draw a picture of the items? Do they use numbers?

DIFFERENTIATION: Supporting the Range of Learners

Intervention Some students may have difficulty counting a group of more than ten objects. If students are unfamiliar with the names of the numbers, do some counting above ten together on the number line and then count the cubes together. If students seem to be having difficulty keeping track of which cubes they have already counted, demonstrate moving each cube as they count it to an "already counted" pile.

DISCUSSION

5 MIN   CLASS

3 Checking In

Take this opportunity to discuss any difficulties that you noticed while observing students at work. The topic may be mathematical in nature, such as a strategy you would like all students to consider (e.g., keeping track of cubes while counting) or a common error or misconception you would like students to discuss (e.g., students' measuring something other than the length of the shoes).

The difficulty may be logistical (e.g., sharing strategies for how to trace a shoe, recording the names of the people the shoes belong to) or management-related (e.g., noise level, working with a partner).

Other alternatives include checking in with students about which activities they have been choosing (e.g., "Thumbs up if you worked on Measuring Shoes; thumbs up if you worked on the Counting Jar"), asking everyone to hold up a piece of work, or allowing students to raise a question or make a comment about today's math class.

SESSION FOLLOW-UP

4 Practice and Homework

 Student Math Handbook Flip Chart: Use the *Student Math Handbook Flip Chart* pages 36, 38 to reinforce concepts from today's session. See pages 186–190 in the back of this unit.

 Homework: Students who are interested can trace around the shoes of people at home. If they like, they can label them and add them to the shoe outlines to be measured during Measuring Shoes.

Measuring with Sticks

Math Focus Points

◆ Repeating multiple nonstandard units to quantify length

◆ Recording measurements with pictures, numbers, and/or words

◆ Counting a set of objects and creating an equivalent set

Today's Plan		Materials
ACTIVITY **① Introducing Measuring with Sticks**	🕐 5–10 MIN 👥 CLASS	• M5* • Labeled strips of wide ribbon (or adding machine tape, masking, or colored electric tape)*; craft sticks
MATH WORKSHOP **② Tracing, Measuring, and Counting** ㉧ Measuring with Sticks ㉨ Tracing Your Shoe ㉩ Measuring Shoes ㉪ Counting Jar	🕐 20–30 MIN	㉧ • *Student Activity Book,* p. 27* • M5* • Materials from Activity 1 ㉨ • Materials from Session 1.2, p. 33 ㉩ • Materials from Session 1.2, p. 33 ㉪ • Materials from Session 1.2, p. 33
DISCUSSION **③ Checking In**	🕐 5 MIN 👥 CLASS	
SESSION FOLLOW-UP **④ Practice**		• *Student Math Handbook Flip Chart,* pp. 36, 38

*See *Materials to Prepare,* p. 25.

Classroom Routines

Today's Question: Do You Have a Younger Brother? On chart paper, create a two-column table titled "Do you have a younger brother?" with the heading "Yes" written at the top of one column and "No" at the top of the other column. Students respond by writing their names below the appropriate heading. Count the responses as a class and discuss what the results of the survey tell you. Continue to ask about and experiment with different ways to organize the data so that it is easier to tell which group has more.

ACTIVITY

① Introducing Measuring with Sticks

5–10 MIN CLASS

Tape Strip A to an area where you can gather students around it. Show students the strip and a handful of craft sticks.

How could we use these craft sticks to measure the length of Strip A, and find out how long it is?

Ask a volunteer to demonstrate his or her ideas. As with the cubes, some students do not line up the end of the first stick with the end of the tape strip, and others overlap sticks or leave gaps between them. Encourage students to watch carefully and to comment on the strategies they are seeing, but allow such inaccuracies to happen. They will form the basis for ongoing conversations about how to measure.

A student uses craft sticks to measure a piece of ribbon while her classmates observe.

Gather a few ideas about how students might record such information.

[Jae] said that Strip A is [5] craft sticks long. How could we record what [Jae] found out?

Model two or three suggestions, including ones that use pictures or numbers to show how many sticks, on the board or on chart paper.

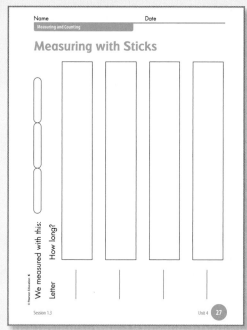

▲ Student Activity Book, p. 27; Resource Masters, M5

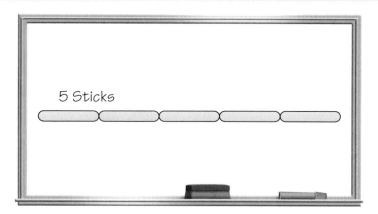

[Cindy] had a different idea about how to use the craft sticks to measure Strip A. Let's try [Cindy's] idea. Do you think we will get the same number?

If the student gets a different number, ask the class to think about this.

[Jae] thinks Strip A is 5 craft sticks long, and [Cindy] thinks it is 4 craft sticks long. What do you think about that? Could both numbers be right?

Although some students will not be bothered by two results or will not know why this may happen, others will have ideas.

Students might say:

 "I think the sticks shouldn't have spaces between them."

 "I think the sticks should start at the beginning of the ribbon."

Expect a wide range in Kindergarten. Some students may be starting to grasp the idea that measuring in different ways can give different measurements, but others may not yet be ready to see this.

Show students the lengths you have placed around the classroom, and explain that measuring these strips with craft sticks will be a Math Workshop activity for the next few days. Explain that, after they measure one of the tapes, students need to record what they find out on *Student Activity Book* page 27.

Model how to record the letter of Strip A and the number of sticks they used to measure it on Measuring with Sticks (M5).

20–30 MIN

② Tracing, Measuring, and Counting

Explain that the following four activities are available during Math Workshop. Remind students what each activity entails, what materials are required, and where they are located.

All students should finish tracing their shoe by the end of this session.

②A Measuring with Sticks

PAIRS

Pairs use craft sticks to measure the lengths of various strips. They use numbers, pictures, and/or words to record their results on *Student Activity Book* page 27.

A student measures a strip that is not exactly the length of the craft sticks.

ONGOING ASSESSMENT: Observing Students at Work

Students repeat a nonstandard unit (craft sticks) to measure length.

- **How do students use craft sticks to measure?** Do they align the end of the first stick with the end of the strip? Do they line up the other sticks end to end, or do they overlap them or leave gaps? Are the sticks laid out in a straight line along the strip, or are they crooked?

- **How do students count and keep track of the number of craft sticks?**

- **How do students record their measurements?** Do they use pictures? Numbers? Words? Some combination of these?

- **What do students do when a length is not close to a whole number of craft sticks?**

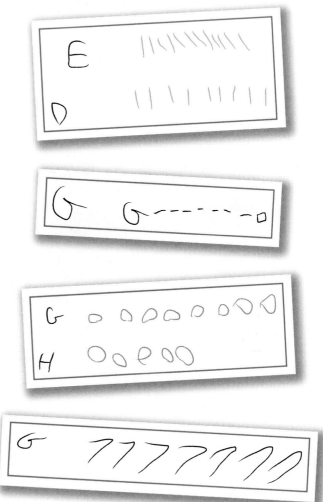

Students measure the length of strips with craft sticks and record their results in a variety of ways.

DIFFERENTIATION: Supporting the Range of Learners

Intervention Some students do not yet understand what it means to measure something with multiple units. They may use the craft sticks to make a design or pattern on the tape or may be unsure about how to use craft sticks to measure. Ask these students to compare the length of strips that are obviously different and decide which is longer. Ask whether it would take more craft sticks to go from one end to the other of the first strip or the second. Then, encourage students to find out.

2B Tracing Your Shoe

PAIRS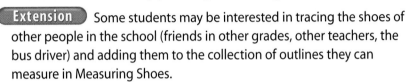

For complete details about this activity, see Session 1.2, page 35.

DIFFERENTIATION: Supporting the Range of Learners

Extension Some students may be interested in tracing the shoes of other people in the school (friends in other grades, other teachers, the bus driver) and adding them to the collection of outlines they can measure in Measuring Shoes.

2C Measuring Shoes

INDIVIDUALS

For complete details about this activity, see Session 1.2, page 35.

Label and then add any shoe outlines students made at home to the collection of outlines students can measure.

DIFFERENTIATION: Supporting the Range of Learners

Extension Once students have measured a number of shoes, they may want to make a list of the shoes from shortest to longest.

2D Counting Jar

INDIVIDUALS

For complete details about this activity, see Session 1.2, page 36.

DISCUSSION

5 MIN   CLASS

③ Checking In

Take this opportunity to discuss any difficulties that you noticed while observing students at work. The topic may be mathematical in nature, such as a strategy you would like all students to consider (e.g., different ways to record measurements, what to do if a length is not close to a whole number of craft sticks) or a common error or misconception you would like students to discuss (e.g., miscounting the craft sticks).

The difficulty may be logistical (e.g., keeping track of which strips have been measured already and which have not) or management-related (e.g., moving around the room to measure strips without disturbing others).

Other alternatives include checking in with students about which activities they have been choosing (e.g., "Who has already had a chance to measure shoes? Who still needs to do the Counting Jar?"), asking everyone to hold up a piece of work, or allowing students to raise a question or make a comment about today's math class.

SESSION FOLLOW-UP

④ Practice

 Student Math Handbook Flip Chart: Use the *Student Math Handbook Flip Chart* pages 36, 38 to reinforce concepts from today's session. See pages 186–190 in the back of this unit.

Comparing Lengths of Shoes

Math Focus Points

◆ Repeating multiple nonstandard units to quantify length

◆ Recording measurements with pictures, numbers, and/or words

◆ Comparing lengths of different objects

Today's Plan	Materials
MATH WORKSHOP **1 Measuring Shoes and Strips** 1A Measuring with Sticks 1B Measuring Shoes 1C Counting Jar *20–35 MIN*	1A • Materials from Session 1.3, p. 38 • Alternative measuring tools 1B • Materials from Session 1.2, p. 33 1C • Materials from Session 1.2, p. 33
DISCUSSION **2 Comparing Lengths of Shoes** *10 MIN CLASS*	• Completed *Student Activity Book,* p. 26 or M4
SESSION FOLLOW-UP **3 Practice**	• *Student Math Handbook Flip Chart,* pp. 36, 38

Classroom Routines

Patterns on the Pocket Chart: What Comes Next? Arrange an ABAB repeating pattern on the pocket chart, using ten Arrow Cards (up, down, up, down). Follow the basic *Patterns* activity. Students point in the direction that they think is under each Question Mark Card.

Measuring Shoes and Strips

20–35 MIN

Explain that the following three activities are available during Math Workshop. Remind students what each activity entails, what materials are required, and where they are located.

All students need to visit Measuring Shoes by the end of this Math Workshop so that they can discuss their findings at the end of the session.

1A Measuring with Sticks

PAIRS

For complete details about this activity, see Session 1.3, page 39.

DIFFERENTIATION: Supporting the Range of Learners

Extension Students who have measured all of the tapes with craft sticks can investigate what happens when they measure them with a tool that is a bit longer (unsharpened pencils, long straws) or a bit shorter (new crayons, short straws) than the craft sticks.

1B Measuring Shoes

INDIVIDUALS

For complete details about this activity, see Session 1.2, page 35.

To prepare for the discussion, look for shoe outlines that many students have measured and that resulted in a variety of answers.

1C Counting Jar

INDIVIDUALS

For complete details about this activity, see Session 1.2, page 36.

Comparing Lengths of Shoes

10 MIN CLASS

Math Focus Points for Discussion

◆ Comparing lengths of different objects

Display the complete set of shoe outlines so that they are clearly visible. Ask students to refer to their completed copies of *Student Activity Book* page 26 (or M4).

Which shoes were the longest? Which were the shortest?

Look together at the suggested outlines and discuss the measurements students got for those shoes.

How many cubes long was the longest shoe you measured? Did anyone find a shoe that was longer than [9] cubes?

How many cubes long was the shortest shoe you measured? Did anyone find a shoe that was shorter than [6] cubes?

If time permits, work together to put the shoe outlines in order from shortest to longest. Use students' recorded measurements and direct comparison to put the outlines in order. If different numbers are shared for the same outline, discuss why this may have happened. Some students may be ready to see that *how* you measure matters. Others will not be bothered by different numbers or may have no idea why this happens. Keep in mind that students will have many opportunities to make sense of this idea over the course of the primary grades.

Students figure out which shoes were the longest and which were the shortest.

SESSION FOLLOW-UP

Practice

Student Math Handbook Flip Chart: Use the *Student Math Handbook Flip Chart* pages 36, 38 to reinforce concepts from today's session. See pages 186–190 in the back of this unit.

Measuring with Cubes

Math Focus Points

◆ Repeating multiple nonstandard units to quantify length

◆ Counting a set of objects and creating an equivalent set

◆ Recording measurements with pictures, numbers, and/or words

Today's Plan		Materials
① ACTIVITY **Introducing Measuring with Cubes**	🕐 5–10 MIN 👥 CLASS	• M8* • Collection of about 10 common objects*; connecting cubes
② MATH WORKSHOP **Measuring with Cubes and Sticks** **②Ⓐ** Measuring with Cubes **②Ⓑ** Measuring with Sticks **②Ⓒ** Counting Jar	🕐 15–25 MIN	**2A** • *Student Activity Book*, p. 28 • M8*; M3* ☑ • 2–3 collections of about 10 common objects; connecting cubes **2B** • Materials from Session 1.3, p. 38 **2C** • Materials from Session 1.2, p. 33
③ DISCUSSION **Comparing Measurements**	🕐 10 MIN 👥 CLASS	• *Student Activity Book*, p. 27 or M5 (from Session 1.3) • Craft sticks
④ SESSION FOLLOW-UP **Practice**		• *Student Activity Book*, p. 29

*See *Materials to Prepare*, p. 27.

Classroom Routines

Attendance: What If We Start With . . . ? As usual, count around the circle to determine the total number of students present today. Then ask students what they think would happen if the count began with a different student and why. Choose a different student to start, count again, and discuss what happens.

ACTIVITY

Introducing Measuring with Cubes

5–10 MIN CLASS

Display one of the collections of objects. Explain that during Math Workshop, students will use cubes to measure the length of a variety of objects. Hold up an object for which the length dimension is obvious, such as a pencil or envelope.

How could we use cubes to measure how long this [pencil] is?

Ask a few volunteers to demonstrate their ideas and ask the class to think and talk about the methods used.

Model how to record the length of the objects using Measuring with Cubes (M8). Some students prefer to draw the objects, and others copy the labels (or letters) from the objects.

You and your partner will choose a collection of objects. Then, you will choose an object and use cubes to measure the length of it. When you and your partner agree on how many cubes long it is, you write what you found out on your recording sheets. Then, choose another object from the collection, and do the same thing.

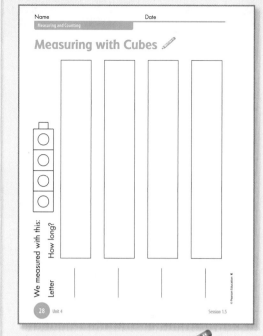

▲ **Student Activity Book, p. 28;**
Resource Masters, M8

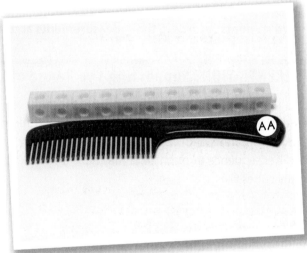

Students use cube towers to measure objects.

❶ **Continuing to Assess Students as They Measure Lengths** Given that students are expected to be able to measure the length of an object by lining up multiple units (Benchmark 1) by the end of this unit, and that they have spent 4 sessions working on measurement activities, this is a good place to look closely at students' strategies. Use M3, Assessment Checklist: Measuring Lengths to keep track of your observations.

Professional Development

❷ **Teacher Note:** Counting Is More Than 1, 2, 3, p. 170 and Observing Kindergarteners as They Count, p. 171

MATH WORKSHOP

② Measuring with Cubes and Sticks

15–25 MIN

Explain that the following three activities are available during Math Workshop. Remind students what each activity entails, what materials are required, and where they are located.

②A Measuring with Cubes

PAIRS

Students use cubes to measure the lengths of classroom objects. They record their results on *Student Activity Book* page 28.

ONGOING ASSESSMENT: Observing Students at Work

Students repeat nonstandard units (cubes) to measure length.❶

- **How do students use cubes to measure?** Do they measure the longest dimension? Do they link the cubes together? Do they hold the cube tower straight and align the end of it with the end of the object?

- **How accurate are students as they count?** How many cubes can they comfortably count? Fewer than 10? Fewer than 15?

- **Are students recording their measurements accurately?**

DIFFERENTIATION: Supporting the Range of Learners

Intervention Keep in mind that some of the items in these collections require students to count up to 20 cubes. Some students need support to count amounts of this size. For example, they may not know the number sequence through 20 or may have trouble keeping track of so many cubes.❷

②B Measuring with Sticks

INDIVIDUALS

For complete details about this activity, see Session 1.3, page 39.

To prepare for the discussion, look for strips that many students measured and that resulted in a variety of answers.

②C Counting Jar

INDIVIDUALS

For complete details about this activity, see Session 1.2, page 36.

Professional Development

❸ **Dialogue Box:** Measuring with Sticks, p. 181

❹ **Teacher Note:** Learning About Length: Lining Up Units, p. 169

DISCUSSION
③ Comparing Measurements

🕙 **10 MIN** 👥 **CLASS**

Math Focus Points for Discussion

◆ Repeating multiple nonstandard units to quantify length

Choose a strip that many students measured and that resulted in a variety of answers.

Who measured the tape along this [desk, Strip G]? How many craft sticks did you use? Did anyone get something else?

Record the different measurements on the board or chart paper.

Why do you suppose we got some different measurements for the same strip of tape?

Students might say:

"Someone could have counted wrong."

"Maybe people measured different. They line up the sticks different."

If you think students would feel comfortable sharing their methods of measuring and having their classmates comment on their methods, ask two students who got different measurements for the strip to do so, one at a time, and ask the class to watch what they do carefully. Otherwise, tell students that you are going to demonstrate two different ways of measuring that you saw students use. You may leave lots of gaps between the sticks as you measure once and then put the craft sticks end to end in a straight line the second time. Ask students to watch carefully what you do and to count the number of craft sticks in each method.❸❹

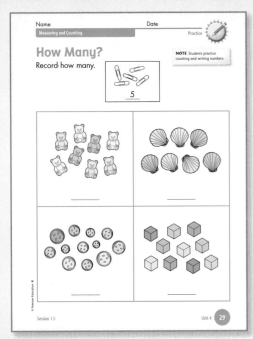

▲ Student Activity Book, p. 29

Why did I get two different numbers?

Students might say:

"There's a lot space between the sticks."

"Yeah, and in that one, the sticks are right next to each other."

Does it matter whether I get two different measurements?

Some students will understand that the length of an object stays the same and that the measurement of its length should be the same each time if using the same materials. They may realize that students got different measurements for the same strip because they measured differently in some way. The fact that students got different measurements for the length of the same object may not bother other students as they do not yet understand that the measurement of a length should stay constant. Students will work a lot more on this idea in first and second grade.

SESSION FOLLOW-UP

Practice

 Practice: For reinforcement of this unit's content, have students complete *Student Activitiy Book* page 29.

Mathematical Emphases

Counting and Quantity Developing strategies for accurately counting a set of objects by ones

Math Focus Points

◆ Connecting number words, numerals, and quantities

◆ Counting a set of objects and creating an equivalent set

◆ Keeping track of a growing set of objects

Whole Number Operations Making sense of and developing strategies to solve addition and subtraction problems with small numbers

Math Focus Points

◆ Finding the total after a small amount (1, 2, 3) is added to a set of up to 7

◆ Combining two amounts

Whole Number Operations Using manipulatives, drawings, tools, and notation to show strategies and solutions

Math Focus Points

◆ Using numbers to represent quantities

◆ Using a Ten-Frame to develop visual images of quantities up to 10

Counting Some, Counting More

	Student Activity Book	Student Math Handbook Flip Chart	Professional Development: Read Ahead of Time	
SESSION 2.1 p. 58				
Revisiting Counting Students revisit *Build It* and learn a variation of *Grab and Count* that involves finding the total of two handfuls of cubes. They also continue to use cubes to measure the length of various objects.	30–31	11–14, 19	• **Teacher Notes:** Counting Is More Than 1, 2, 3, p. 170; Observing Kindergarteners as They Count, p. 171	
SESSION 2.2 p. 65				
Collect 10 Together Students learn, play, and discuss *Collect 10 Together*. In this game, players roll a 1-to-3 dot cube to accumulate pennies until they have 10. Math Workshop focuses on measuring and counting.	30	11		
SESSION 2.3 p. 71				
Build On Students learn *Build On,* a variation of *Build It.* In this game, players turn over a Primary Number Card, fill a Ten-Frame with that many counters. Then they roll a 1-to-3 dot cube, add that many counters and figure out how many they have altogether. Math Workshop continues to focus on measuring, counting, and finding the total after a small amount is added to a set.	30, 32			
SESSION 2.4 p. 76				
Roll and Record 2 Students learn, play, and discuss a variation of *Roll and Record* in which they roll a 1–6 *and* a 1–3 dot cube and record the total.	33	11		

Classroom Routines See page 20 for an overview.

Calendar	Patterns on the Pocket Chart
• Monthly calendar	• Pocket Chart or Sentence Pocket Chart
Today's Question	• M7, Question Mark Cards (from Investigation 1)
• *Today's Question* chart for Session 2.2. See instructions on page 65.	• Square tiles (3 of each color)
Attendance	• Prepared cups or baggies of colored construction paper squares (1 per pair)
• No materials needed	

Materials to Gather	Materials to Prepare
• **Counters** (10 or so) • **Connecting cubes** • **Writing and drawing materials** • **Materials for Measuring with Cubes** See Session 1.5.	• **M9–M12, Primary Number Cards** If you are not using the manufactured decks; make copies on card stock and laminate, if possible. (1 per student; remove Wild Cards) • **M13, Ten-Frame** Make copies. (as needed) • **M14, *Grab and Count: Two Handfuls*** Make copies. (as needed) • **M15, Assessment Checklist: Counting** ☑ Make copies. (3–4 per class, plus extras as needed)
• **Book or books about money or pennies** such as *Benny's Pennies* by Pat Brisson, *A Chair for My Mother* by Vera Williams (also available in Spanish), **and** *Penny* by Jeffrey Patnaude (optional). • **Materials for *Build It*** See Session 2.1. • **Materials for *Grab and Count: Two Handfuls*** See Session 2.1. • **Materials for Measuring with Cubes** See Session 1.5. • **Pennies or other counters** (15–20 per pair)	• **Dot cubes and stick-on dots for making 1-to-3 dot cubes** Cover the 4, 5, and 6 faces of a set of dot cubes with stickers of dots showing 1, 2, and 3 dots. (1 per pair)
• **Counters** (10 or so) • **1-to-3 dot cube** (1) • **One of the longer items** (15 or 20 cubes, 12–15 inches long) from a Measurement Collection • **Connecting cubes** • **Materials for *Collect 10 Together*** See Session 2.2. • **Materials for *Grab and Count: Two Handfuls*** See Session 2.1. • **Materials for Measuring with Cubes** See Session 1.5.	• **M13, Ten-Frame** Make copies. (1 per pair) • **Primary Number Cards** (1 deck per pair; with the 7–10 and Wild Cards removed)
• **1-to-6 dot cubes** (1 per pair) • **1-to-3 dot cubes** (1 per pair)	• **M16, *Roll and Record* 2** Make copies. (as needed)

☑ Checklist Available

Counting Some, Counting More, *continued*

SESSION 2.5 p. 80	Student Activity Book	Student Math Handbook Flip Chart	Professional Development: Read Ahead of Time	
Quick Images: Ten-Frames Students reproduce images of dots arranged in a Ten-Frame. Math Workshop focuses on finding the total after a small amount is added to a set.		11, 12		

Materials to Gather	Materials to Prepare
• **Pennies or other counters** (15–20 per student; 20–25 per pair) • **Materials for doing the Counting Jar routine** (as you have set it up) • **1-to-6 number cubes** (as needed) • **Materials for** *Collect 10* See Session 2.2. • **Materials for** *Roll and Record* **2** See Session 2.4. • **Materials for** *Build On* See Session 2.3.	• **M13,** *Ten-Frame* Make copies. (1 per student) • **M17,** *Quick Images: Ten-Frame* Copy onto a transparency and cut into separate images. • **Counting Jar** Place 15 objects in the jar.

Overhead Transparency

Revisiting Counting

Math Focus Points

◆ Connecting number words, numerals, and quantities

◆ Counting a set of up to 20 objects

◆ Combining two amounts

Today's Plan		Materials
ACTIVITY **1** Introducing *Build It*	5 MIN · CLASS	• M13* • M9–M12* • Counters
ACTIVITY **2** Introducing *Grab and Count: Two Handfuls*	5 MIN · CLASS	• *Student Activity Book*, p. 31 • M13* • Connecting cubes; writing and drawing materials
MATH WORKSHOP **3** Counting and Measuring **3A** *Build It* **3B** *Grab and Count: Two Handfuls* **3C** *Measuring with Cubes*	15–30 MIN	**3A** • *Student Activity Book*, p. 30 • Materials from Activity 1 **3B** • *Student Activity Book*, p. 31 • M14*; M15* ☑ • Materials from Activity 2 **3C** • Materials from Session 1.5, p. 48
DISCUSSION **4** Checking In	5 MIN · CLASS	
SESSION FOLLOW-UP **5** Practice		• *Student Math Handbook Flip Chart*, pp. 11–14, 19

*See *Materials to Prepare*, p. 55.

Classroom Routines

Calendar: How Many Days . . . ? Students use the monthly calendar to determine how many days until a class event or holiday that will happen this month. Discuss students' strategies for determining the number of days.

ACTIVITY 1

5 MIN CLASS

Introducing *Build It*

Ask students what they remember about the game *Build It,* which they played in *Counting and Comparing.* Then play a round or two to reintroduce it, reminding students that they will need a deck of Primary Number Cards (M9–M12), ten or so counters, and a Ten-Frame (M13).

First you turn over a Primary Number Card. [Turn over an 8.] What card did I turn over? How do you know? Now I arrange eight counters on my Ten-Frame.❶

Count out eight counters. Count them again as you place them on the Ten-Frame, filling one complete row before starting the second row.❷

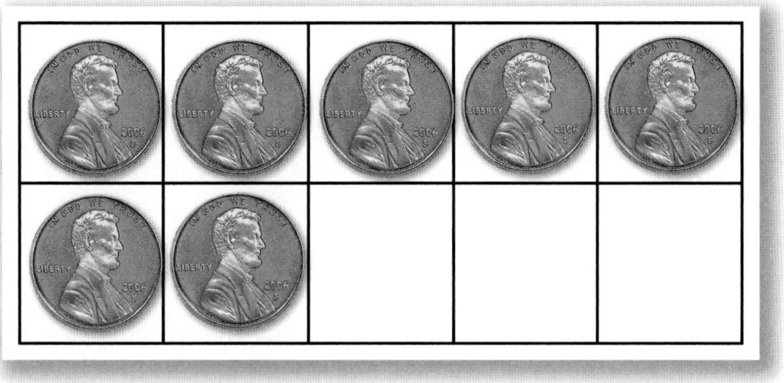

When the class agrees that you have placed as many counters on your Ten-Frame as the number on your Primary Number Card, remove the counters, turn over another Primary Number Card, and demonstrate another round, as needed.

ACTIVITY 2

5 MIN CLASS

Introducing *Grab and Count: Two Handfuls*

Remind students of the *Grab and Count* activities they did in *Counting and Comparing* (unit 2). Explain that today they will be doing a new version of this game.

Ask a volunteer to grab a handful of connecting cubes and place them on the floor or on a table. Nearby, set out a pile of five cubes for reference.

We know that this pile has five cubes. About how many cubes do you think there are in the handful [Beth] grabbed? Does it look like five? More than five? Fewer than five? Let's count and find out.

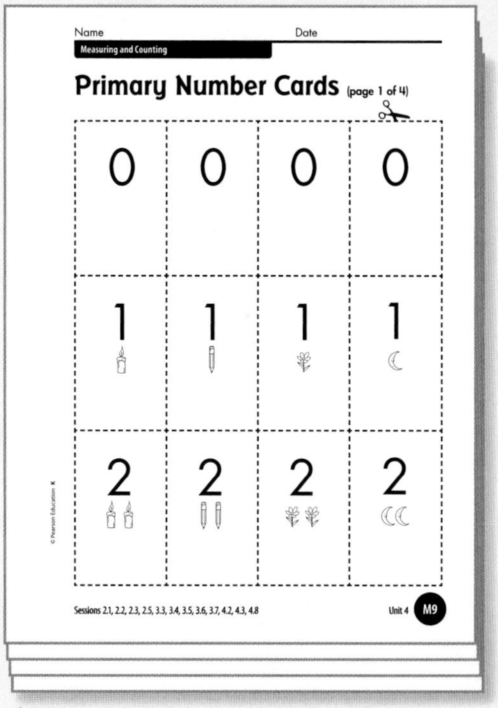

Name Date

Measuring and Counting

Primary Number Cards (page 1 of 4)

0	0	0	0
1	1	1	1
2	2	2	2

© Pearson Education K

Sessions 2.1, 2.2, 2.3, 2.5, 3.3, 3.4, 3.5, 3.6, 3.7, 4.2, 4.3, 4.8

Unit 4 M9

▲ Resource Masters, M9–M12

Teaching Notes

❶ **Reading Written Numbers** Make sure students know that if they don't know the name of the number, they can count the objects on the card to figure it out.

❷ **Different Images of the Same Number** Model one way to place the counters on the Ten-Frame, but know that some students may fill rows of 2.

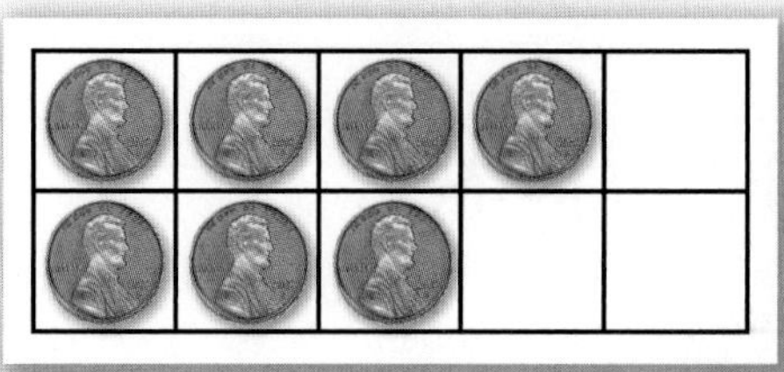

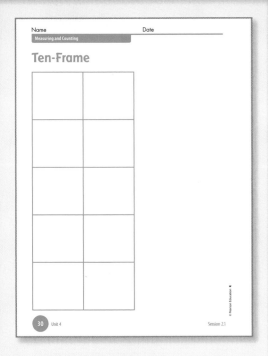

▲ **Student Activity Book, p. 30;**
Resource Masters, M13

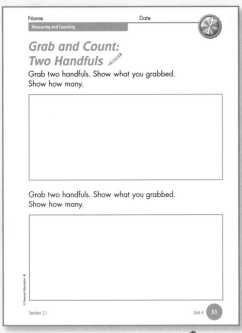

▲ **Student Activity Book, p. 31;**
Resource Masters, M14

Ask a volunteer to count the cubes, or count them together as a class. Snap them together to make a tower.

Today you're going to grab two handfuls of connecting cubes and figure out how many cubes you have altogether. [Beth] grabbed one handful of cubes. Now she's going to grab another handful of cubes.

After the volunteer grabs a second handful, count them and build a second tower.

Now we want to find out how many cubes [Beth] grabbed altogether. What could we do to find out?

Students might say:

"Count the cubes in the first tower and then keep counting the other one."

"You could make one big tower and count it."

Try each of the methods suggested, using the calendar or number line to help students with the names and sequence of the numbers over ten.

Students count the number of cubes in the two towers. The teacher points to the numbers on the number line to help students with counting.

Explain that students will show how many cubes they grabbed in two handfuls on *Student Activity Book* page 31.

What if we wanted to use this paper to show how many cubes [Beth] grabbed in two handfuls? What could we do so that someone looking at her paper could tell how many she grabbed?

Collect a few ideas, such as drawing a picture or writing the number or name of the items, but know that students often develop ideas as they actually do the activity.

MATH WORKSHOP

15–30 MIN

3 Counting and Measuring

Explain that the following three activities are available during Math Workshop. Remind students what each activity entails, what materials are required, and where they are located.

INDIVIDUALS

3A *Build It*

Students turn over a Primary Number Card to find out how many counters to take. Then they arrange the counters on a Ten-Frame (*Student Activity Book* page 30 or M13).

ONGOING ASSESSMENT: Observing Students at Work

Students practice reading the written numbers, creating a set of a given size, and arranging counters in a Ten-Frame.

- **How do students figure out the number on the card?** Do they "just know" the name of the number? Do they count the pictures on the card?

- **Are students accurate in counting the counters?** Do they count them first and then place them on the Ten-Frame? Do they count them as they place them?

❸ Assessment Checklist: Counting By the end of this unit, students are expected to be able to count a set of up to 15 objects (Benchmark 2). This means that they know the number names in sequence, say one number for each object, and have a system for keeping track of what they are counting. Use Assessment Checklist: Counting (M15) to keep track of your observations about students' counting over the course of this unit.

Professional Development

❹ Teacher Note: Counting Is More Than 1, 2, 3, p. 170 and Observing Kindergarteners as They Count, p. 171

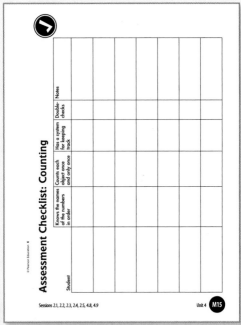

▲ Resource Masters, M15 ✓

- **How do students arrange the counters?** Do any use the structure of the Ten-Frame to help them count (e.g., "One row's 5, so that's 6, 7, 8" or "2, 4, 6, 8" or "4 and 4 is 8" or "The whole thing's 10. Two spaces are empty so 9, 8.")

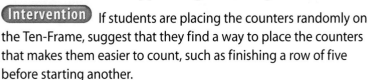

DIFFERENTIATION: Supporting the Range of Learners

Intervention If students are placing the counters randomly on the Ten-Frame, suggest that they find a way to place the counters that makes them easier to count, such as finishing a row of five before starting another.

❸B Grab and Count: Two Handfuls

INDIVIDUALS

Students grab two handfuls of cubes, figure out the total number of cubes they grabbed, and find a way to record how many they grabbed.

ONGOING ASSESSMENT: Observing Students at Work

Students count larger amounts as they find the total of two quantities. ❸ ❹

- **How do students count their handfuls?** Do they count accurately, counting each item once and only once? Do they double-check?

- **How do students find the total of the two handfuls?** Do they count them all from one? Do they count on from one quantity?

- **How do students represent their handfuls?** Do they draw something to represent each cube? Do they use numbers?

Assessment Checklist: Counting

Student	Knows the names of the numbers in order	Counts each object once and only once	Has a system for keeping track	Double-checks	Notes
Kiyo grab & count	✓	✓	✓	no	up to 20
Jennifer grab & count	counts 15 objects missing the number 12	one-to-one up to 6 then says 2 numbers for one cube sometimes	puts cubes in a line	no	needs more work with #s under 10
Kyle grab & count	pauses after 10 I say 11 & he continues accurately	✓	✓	yes pauses after 10 again	
Jae grab & count	✓	✓	no, so double counts some pennies	no	ask him to double ✓ gets a different # which doesn't bother him
Manuel grab & count	looks at number line after 12—says "one three, one four"	✓	✓		doesn't know the names for #s over 12

DIFFERENTIATION: Supporting the Range of Learners

Intervention Students who find counting quantities below ten challenging should practice grabbing, counting, and recording one handful at a time.

3C Measuring with Cubes PAIRS

For complete details about this activity, see Session 1.5, page 49.

 **Extension** Students who have finished measuring the collections of objects, and/or are ready for more challenge can choose other classroom objects to measure or can use cubes to measure longer things, such as the strips of tape from Measuring with Sticks, page 40.

 DISCUSSION

Checking In

5 MIN   CLASS

Take this opportunity to discuss any difficulties that you noticed while observing students at work. The topic may be mathematical in nature, such as a strategy you would like all students to consider (e.g., double-checking a count, different ways to find the total number of cubes in two handfuls) or a common error or misconception you would like students to discuss (e.g., placing the incorrect number of pennies in the Ten-Frame or drawing the incorrect number of cubes on the *Grab and Count* paper).

The difficulty may be logistical (e.g., grabbing a reasonable-sized handful of cubes) or management-related (e.g., sharing bins of cubes with others, choosing an activity).

Other alternatives include checking in with students about which activities they have been choosing (e.g., "Thumbs up if you did *Grab and Count* today. Who still needs to do Measuring with Cubes?"), asking everyone to hold up a piece of work, or allowing students to raise a question or make a comment about today's math class.

 SESSION FOLLOW-UP

Practice

 Student Math Handbook Flip Chart: Use the *Student Math Handbook Flip Chart* pages 11–14, 19 to reinforce concepts from today's session.

Collect 10 Together

Math Focus Points

- Counting a set of objects
- Keeping track of a growing set of objects
- Finding the total after a small amount (1, 2, 3) is added to a set up to 7

Vocabulary

penny
more
less

Today's Plan

		Materials
① ACTIVITY **Introducing** *Collect 10 Together* 5–10 MIN CLASS		• 1-to-3 dot cube*; pennies; book or books about money or pennies (optional)*
② ACTIVITY **Playing** *Collect 10 Together* 5–10 MIN PAIRS		• M13* • 1-to-3 dot cube*; pennies
③ DISCUSSION *Collect 10 Together* 5–10 MIN CLASS		• Materials from Activity 2
④ MATH WORKSHOP **More Counting and Measuring** ④A *Collect 10 Together* ④B *Build It* ④C *Grab and Count: Two Handfuls* ④D *Measuring with Cubes* 15 MIN		④A • Materials from Activity 2 ④B • Materials from Session 2.1, p. 58 ④C • Materials from Session 2.1, p. 58 ④D • Materials from Session 1.5, p. 48
⑤ SESSION FOLLOW-UP **Practice**		• *Student Math Handbook Flip Chart,* pp. 11

*See *Materials to Prepare,* p. 55.

Classroom Routines

Today's Question: Would You Rather Be a Fish or a Butterfly? On chart paper, create a vertical 2-column table titled "Would you rather be a fish or a butterfly?" with the heading "Fish" at the top of one column and "Butterfly" at the top of the other column. Students respond by writing their names below the appropriate heading. Count the responses as a class and discuss what the results of the survey tell you.

Teaching Notes

❶ **Children's Literature** You may want to reinforce the introduction to pennies and money by reading students one of the following stories during literacy: *Benny's Pennies* by Pat Brisson, *A Chair for My Mother* by Vera Williams (also available in Spanish), or *Penny* by Jeffrey Patnaude.

❷ **What's a Penny Worth?** Because many kindergarteners are still developing an understanding of one-to-one correspondence, this concept of what a penny is "worth" can be challenging. You can assure these students that pennies can be thought of like buttons or cubes in that each one is counted once and worth "one."

ACTIVITY

① Introducing *Collect 10 Together*

In *Collect 10 Together*, students collect pennies until they have ten. Begin by giving each pair or small group one penny.❶

Today we're going to learn a new game called *Collect 10 Together*. You are going to count with these. Does anyone know what this is called?

Some students may know the name of a penny. If not, tell students yourself.

This is a penny. What do we use pennies for?

Students might say:

"Pennies are money. We use them to pay for things."

How much is a penny worth?❷

Next, introduce *Collect 10 Together* by playing a demonstration game. Play one or two complete games to make sure that students understand the rules.

The goal of *Collect 10 Together* is for two players to work together to collect 10 pennies. Partners take turns rolling a dot cube and taking as many pennies as there are dots on the cube.

Ask a volunteer to inspect the dot cube and tell the class about it. When you have established that there are 1, 2, and 3 dots on the sides of the cube, ask one player and then another to roll the cube.

Students roll the dot cube and then take the same number of pennies as displayed on the dot cube.

What did [Tammy] roll? How many counters should [Tammy] take? How do you know? What did [Brad] roll? How many counters should he take? How do you know?

After each player has rolled and everyone has agreed on how many counters to take, talk about the growing set.

Do you think [Tammy] and [Brad] have ten pennies yet? Why do you think so? How many do they have? How do you know?

Students might say:

 "I counted 1, 2, 3, 4. 4 is smaller than 10."

 "They both took 2 pennies. 2 and 2 makes 4. And 4 is less than 10."

 "Tammy has 2. Brad's pennies makes 3, 4."

Where in our classroom could we find out whether four is more or less than ten? How else could you compare four and ten to see which is more?

The game is over as soon as players have at least ten pennies. Depending on what they roll at the end, they may get ten exactly, or they may end up with more than ten.

ACTIVITY

5–10 MIN   PAIRS

2 Playing *Collect 10 Together*

Students play *Collect 10 Together* in pairs.

ONGOING ASSESSMENT: Observing Students at Work

Students count and keep track of a growing set of objects as they work to create a set of a given size (10).

- **Do students need to count the dots to see how many pennies to take?** Do they take the same number of pennies as dots on the cube?

- **How do students find the total number of pennies after new ones have been added?** Do they count them from 1? Count on from the number they had at the end of the last turn? Do they "just know" some combinations that are 1 (or 2, or 3) more?

- **Do students know how many more pennies they need to have 10?** Do they recognize when they have 10? When they have more than 10?

As students work, ask them questions that focus on the important mathematical ideas in this game.

- How many pennies do you have now? How do you know?

- How many more pennies do you think you need to have 10?

DIFFERENTIATION: Supporting the Range of Learners

Intervention Some students find a Ten-Frame useful for keeping track of the pennies. If students are having difficulty counting amounts to ten, change the game to *Collect 7* or *8 Together*.

DISCUSSION

3 *Collect 10 Together*

5–10 MIN   CLASS

Math Focus Points for Discussion

◆ Keeping track of a growing set of objects

Bring students together to discuss how they are figuring out the total number of pennies after each turn.

Everyone has had a chance to play Collect 10 Together for a little while. I am interested in how you are figuring out how many pennies you have after each roll. Let's play a couple of rounds.

Ask a volunteer to roll the dot cube and count out that many pennies. Then ask another volunteer to do the same.

We had [three] pennies. Then [Jason] rolled a [two] and added [two] more pennies. How can we figure out how many pennies we have altogether?

Students might say:

 "Count them, 1, 2, 3, 4, 5."

 "We had 3, so 2 more is 4, 5."

Ask students to model their strategies. If a student counts on, ask the class about that.

I noticed that [Mary] did something interesting. She used something she knew. [Mary] remembered that we had [three] pennies before [gesture over the pile of three] and said, "We had [three], now we have [two] more, so [four], [five]. There's [five] pennies." She didn't even count these [three] pennies. Can she do that? Doesn't she need to count *all* the pennies?

Although some students may be counting on or may begin to experiment with it, expect others to continue to count all each time they need to find the total.

 MATH WORKSHOP

4 More Counting and Measuring

 15 MIN

Explain that the following four activities are available during Math Workshop. Remind students what each activity entails, what materials are required, and where they are located.

If any students have yet to revisit *Build It,* they should do so today because a new variation of this activity is introduced at the beginning of Session 2.3.

 4A *Collect 10 Together*

 PAIRS

For complete details about this activity, see Session 2.2, page 67.

4B **Build It**

INDIVIDUALS

For complete details about this activity, see Session 2.1, page 59.

4C **Grab and Count: Two Handfuls**

INDIVIDUALS

For complete details about this activity, see Session 2.1, page 59.

DIFFERENTIATION: Supporting the Range of Learners

Extension Students who easily find the total of two handfuls of cubes can try one of the following two variations:

● Grab two handfuls of smaller objects, which will result in larger quantities.

● Grab three or more handfuls of cubes and find the total.

4D **Measuring with Cubes**

PAIRS

For complete details about this activity, see Session 1.5, page 49.

SESSION FOLLOW-UP

5 Practice

 Student Math Handbook Flip Chart: Use the *Student Math Handbook Flip Chart* page 11 to reinforce concepts from today's session. See pages 186–190 in the back of this unit.

Build On

Math Focus Points

- Connecting number words, numerals, and quantities
- Counting a set of objects and creating an equivalent set
- Finding the total after a small amount (1, 2, 3) is added to a set of up to 7

Today's Plan		Materials
ACTIVITY **①** **Introducing *Build On***	🕐 5–10 MIN 👥 CLASS	• M13* • Primary Number Cards*; counters; 1-to-3 dot cube
MATH WORKSHOP **②** **How Many Counters? How Many Cubes?** **2A** *Build On* **2B** *Collect 10 Together* **2C** *Grab and Count: Two Handfuls* **2D** *Measuring with Cubes*	🕐 15–25 MIN	**2A** • Materials from Activity 1 **2B** • Materials from Session 2.2, p. 65 **2C** • Materials from Session 2.1, p. 58 **2D** • Materials from Session 1.5, p. 48
DISCUSSION **③** **Counting Strategies**	🕐 10 MIN 👥 CLASS	• One of the longer items (15–20 cubes, 12–15 inches long) from a Measurement Collection; connecting cubes
SESSION FOLLOW-UP **④** **Practice**		• *Student Activity Book*, p. 32

*See *Materials to Prepare*, p. 55.

Classroom Routines

Patterns on the Pocket Chart: What Comes Next? Arrange an ABCD repeating pattern on the pocket chart, using ten square tiles (red, blue, green, yellow). Follow the basic *Patterns* activity. Students hold up the colored construction paper square that they think is under each Question Mark Card.

ACTIVITY

1 Introducing *Build On*

Today, you'll learn how to play *Build On*, a game that's similar to *Build It*. You'll work with a partner for *Build On*.

Ask a volunteer to play a few rounds with you to introduce the game to the class.

The first step of *Build On* is the same as *Build It*. Player 1 turns over the top card and places that many counters on the Ten-Frame (M13). What number did [Timothy] turn over? [4] How many counters should he place on our Ten-Frame? [4]

Now it's Player 2's turn. Player 2 rolls the 1-to-3 dot cube to see how many counters to add to the Ten-Frame. What did I roll? [2] I need to add [2] more counters.

[Timothy] put [4] counters on our Ten-Frame and I added [2] more. Now our job is to work together to figure out how many counters there are altogether. How could [Timothy] and I figure out how many counters we have altogether?

Students might say:

 "We could count them. 1, 2, 3, 4, 5, 6."

 "We started with 4, so we can just count the ones you added. [Pointing] 5, 6."

 "There's 1 row of 5 and 1 more. 5 and 1 more is 6."

Try each strategy that students suggest. Have students demonstrate their ideas for their classmates or model them yourself, occasionally wondering aloud whether each strategy will give you the same results.

[Rebecca] said that there were [4] counters and [2] more makes [pointing to the 5th counter] [5], [pointing to 6th counter] [6] counters. [Abby] said to count them all. How many do you think there will be if we count them all? Let's try it.

Play another round, changing roles with your partner. Play enough rounds that students understand how to play.

 MATH WORKSHOP

How Many Counters? How Many Cubes?

15–25 MIN

Explain that the following four activities are available during Math Workshop and that today is the last day that Measuring with Cubes will be available. Remind students what each activity entails, what materials are required, and where they are located.

. . . .

 Build On

PAIRS

Player 1 turns over a Primary Number Card and arranges that many counters on a Ten-Frame. Then, Player 2 rolls a 1-to-3 dot cube and adds that many counters to the Ten-Frame. Finally, players work together to figure out how many counters are on the Ten-Frame altogether.

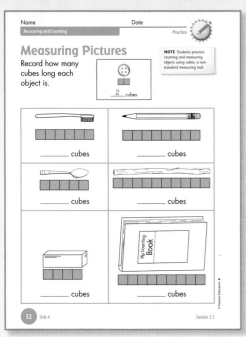

▲ Student Activity Book, p. 32

Students read the written numbers, create a set of a given size, and find the total when 1, 2, or 3 is added to that set.

- **How do students figure out the number on the card?** Do they "just know" the name of the number? Do they count the pictures on the card?

- **Are students accurate in their counting?** How do students arrange the counters on the Ten-Frame?

- **How do students find the total after 1, 2, or 3 has been added?** Do they count all? Count on? Use number combinations they know (e.g., "We had 3 and rolled a 3. I know that 3 and 3 is 6")? Use the structure of the Ten-Frame (e.g., "This row has 5 and 1 more is 6")?

DIFFERENTIATION: Supporting the Range of Learners

Intervention If some students are placing the counters randomly on the Ten-Frame, suggest that they find a way to place the counters that makes them easier to count, such as finishing a row (of two or five) before starting another.

2B *Collect 10 Together*

PAIRS

For complete details about this activity, see Session 2.2, page 66.

2C *Grab and Count: Two Handfuls*

INDIVIDUALS

For complete details about this activity, see Session 2.1, page 59.

2D *Measuring with Cubes*

PAIRS

For complete details about this activity, see Session 1.5, page 49.

DISCUSSION
③ Counting Strategies

10 MIN   CLASS

Math Focus Points for Discussion

◆ Counting a set of up to 20 objects

Focus this discussion on one of the longer objects from a measurement collection, one that measures between 15 and 20 cubes.

Ask students which dimension you should measure if you want to find out how long the object is. Then, link cubes together along this dimension.❶

When students are in agreement that you have a tower that is as long as your object, focus the discussion on the number of cubes in the tower.

Look at all of these cubes! I wonder how many cubes there are in my tower?

Ask several students to count the cubes in your tower. Reassure them that there are many cubes, and that everyone is still learning to count amounts this large. They should feel free to ask for help if, for example, they do not know the name of the next number. The class should watch closely as your volunteer counts.

*What did you notice about the way [Carmen] counted the cubes? What about the way [Dennis] counted the cubes?*❷

Discuss the strategies students use, and use helpful counting strategies when you count the cubes together as a class.

[Raul] said that you have to say one number for each cube, and [Emma] said that it helps her if she touches each cube as she counts it. Let's count them together. I'll touch the cubes, as [Emma] suggested, and we'll try to do what [Raul] said and say one number for each cube. Are you ready?

Count the cubes another time or two, perhaps starting at the other end of the tower, so that students hear the number sequence several times.❸

SESSION FOLLOW-UP
④ Practice

Practice: For reinforcement of this unit's content, have students complete *Student Activity Book* page 32.

Teaching Note

❶ **Assessing Measurement Techniques** If you want more information about how your students are making sense of linear measurement, make purposeful mistakes as you measure the object; for example, do not link the cubes together and/or lay the tower diagonally. Encourage students to explain what you are doing wrong and to model the correct way to do it.

Math Note

❷ **Can It Be 12 and 15?** Because there are so many cubes, students may end up with different totals. Encourage students to think about whether this is permissible and why it may happen, but realize that some five- and six-year-olds do not yet see a number as a stable quantity that should not change if nothing has been added or taken away.

Professional Development

❸ **Teacher Notes:** Counting Is More Than 1, 2, 3, p. 170 and Observing Kindergarteners as They Count, p. 171

Roll and Record 2

Math Focus Points

◆ Finding the total after a small amount (1, 2, 3) is added to a set of up to 6

◆ Connecting number words, numerals, and quantities

◆ Using numbers to represent quantities

Today's Plan		Materials
① ACTIVITY **Introducing** *Roll and Record 2*	5–10 MIN CLASS	• M16* • 1-to-6 dot cubes; 1-to-3 dot cubes
② ACTIVITY **Playing** *Roll and Record 2*	15–25 MIN PAIRS	• *Student Activity Book*, p. 33 • M16* • 1-to-6 dot cubes; 1-to-3 dot cubes
③ DISCUSSION *Roll and Record 2*	10 MIN CLASS	• Materials from Activity 2
④ SESSION FOLLOW-UP **Practice**		• *Student Math Handbook Flip Chart*, p. 11

*See *Materials to Prepare*, p. 55

Classroom Routines

Attendance: Comparing Groups Count around the circle as usual, and then count the number of boys and the number of girls in class today. Ask students whether there are more boys or girls. Have the boys make a line and the girls make a line opposite them. Count the number of students in each line and again ask whether there are more boys or girls. Challenge students to figure out how many more and discuss their strategies.

ACTIVITY

1 Introducing *Roll and Record 2*

5–10 MIN CLASS

Today you are going to learn how to play a new version of the game, *Roll and Record*. In *Roll and Record 2,* you will roll two dot cubes. Then, just like before, you figure out how much you rolled, and write the total on the recording sheet.

Play several rounds to introduce the game to students.

The first thing you do is roll two dot cubes. [Roll the cubes.] What did I roll? I rolled a [4] and a [1]. Now I have to figure out how many dots there are altogether. How could I do that?

Some students count the dots one by one. Others count on from four or reason about addition combinations they know. Have students demonstrate their ideas for their classmates, or model them yourself occasionally wondering about whether each strategy will give you the same result.

[Manuel] counted these dots [on the 4 cube] and then this dot [on the 1 cube] and got 5 dots altogether. 1, 2, 3, 4, 5. [Hugo] said that he would count the [1] and then the [4]. What number do you think [Hugo] will get? Let's try it.❶

When you agree on the total number of dots, ask where you should record that number.❷

We agree that I got [5] dots altogether, so I need to write [5] on my recording sheet. Where should I write [5]? How do you know? What if I don't know what a [5] looks like? How could I figure out how to write a [5]?❸

Take students' ideas, and then record your roll on *Roll and Record 2* Recording Sheet (M16). Play another round or two, as needed. Just as in *Roll and Record,* the game is finished when one number wins meaning there is a number written in every box in that column.

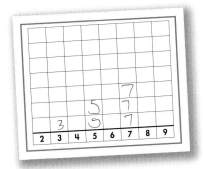

Sample Student Work

Algebra Note

❶ **Does Order Matter When You Count?** Although this was discussed in Unit 1, it will still be in question for some students. Therefore, continue to find opportunities to pose such questions. When students confirm that counting 4 and then 1 gives the same number as counting 1 and then 4, you might ask, "I wonder if the number 5 is special, or does it *always* work to change the order when we count?"

Teaching Notes

❷ **Where Is 1?** If students do not notice, point out that the *Roll and Record 2* recording sheet includes columns for the numbers 2–9. Explain that there is not a 1 column because there is no way to roll a 1 with these dot cubes.

❸ **How Do I Write 5?** When students played *Roll and Record* in Unit 1, some of them counted up on the *Student Activity Book* page from 1 to the 5 to figure out how to write 5. Because there is no 1 on this *Student Activity Book* page, they can no longer do this. Suggest that students use other resources—such as the number line or the calendar—or you can add the number 1 to their recording sheets.

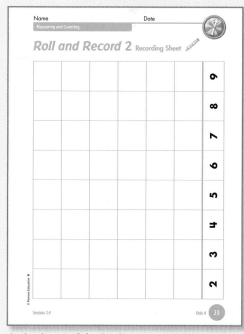

▲ **Student Activity Book, p. 33; Resource Masters, M16**

ACTIVITY

❷ Playing *Roll and Record 2*

15–20 MIN PAIRS

Students roll a 1-to-6 and a 1-to-3 dot cube and write the number rolled on the *Roll and Record 2* recording sheet. ❹

ONGOING ASSESSMENT: Observing Students at Work

Students count and combine small amounts and practice writing the numbers through nine.

- **How do students figure out the total of their roll?** Do they count all of the dots? Count on? Do they "just know" some combinations?

- **How do students figure out where to write their total?** Can they write the numbers accurately?

As you observe, note the strategies students use to combine their rolls and discuss these at the end of this session.

DIFFERENTIATION: Supporting the Range of Learners

Intervention Because the dot cubes are small, some students may count more accurately if they use counters to recreate the dot images. If students are having difficulty accurately forming the numbers, make this a focus of your handwriting curriculum.

Extension Students often become very interested in which number "wins." Although the goal of this game is connecting numbers and quantities, you can ask these students questions about their completed game *Student Activity Book* page; for example, "Which number did you roll the most times?" and "How many times did you roll a seven?"

DISCUSSION

❸ Roll and Record 2

10 MIN CLASS

Math Focus Points for Discussion

◆ Finding the total after a small amount (1, 2, 3) is added to a set of up to 6

Call students together to discuss how they are finding the total when they roll two dot cubes.

In this game, you roll two dot cubes and then figure out how many dots there are altogether. I'm curious about how people are figuring out the total number of dots.

Roll a 1-to-6 and a 1-to-3 dot cube to generate a problem. Ask students to look at your roll and think quietly about how they would figure out what number to write on their recording sheet.

Call on students on the basis of your observations while students played in pairs. Begin with a student who recreates the dot images with counters and then counts them.

[Cindy], I noticed that when you were playing, you used counters to help you figure out how many dots there were. Could you show us how you were using the counters?

Also ask a student or two to model counting all of the dots by 1s. Continue to ask questions that push students to think about whether order matters when they count.

[Victor] counted the [2] and then the [5]. [Corey] said that she would count the [5] first and then the [2]. Can she do that? Will she get the same answer as [Victor]?

Expect a range of responses. Some students think it matters; others are sure that it does not. A few students may say that, although it does not affect your answer, it is easier to start with the larger amount and then count the smaller amount. These students may be counting on to add small amounts, or close to it.

Ask a student who counts on to show how he or she would solve the problem.

I noticed something interesting today. I was watching [Jennifer] play, and when she rolls a [5] and a [2], she counts like this. [5] [point to the dot cube showing 5]; [6], [7] [point to each dot on the dot cube showing 2]. Can she do that? I didn't hear her count these dots [point to the dot cube showing 5].❺

Math Note

❺ **Counting On** As students begin to combine small quantities, most students count from one to find the total. Some may count on from one quantity during Kindergarten ("This cube is 4, and this one is 3, so 5, 6, 7. I got 7.") but may not count on consistently until first grade.

SESSION FOLLOW-UP

Practice

Student Math Handbook Flip Chart: Use the *Student Math Handbook Flip Chart* page 11 to reinforce concepts from today's session.

Quick Images: Ten-Frames

Math Focus Points

◆ Using a Ten-Frame to develop visual images of quantities up to 10

◆ Finding the total after a small amount (1, 2, 3) is added to a set of up to 7

◆ Connecting number words, numerals, and quantities

Vocabulary
image(s)

Today's Plan			Materials
① ACTIVITY *Quick Images: Ten-Frames*	10–15 MIN	CLASS	• M13* • M17* • Pennies or other counters
② MATH WORKSHOP **Counting Activities** **2A** Counting Jar **2B** Collect 15 Together **2C** Roll and Record 2 **2D** Build On	15–25 MIN		**2A** • M15* ☑ • Counting Jar* • Materials for doing the Counting Jar routine (as you have set it up) **2B** • M13* Materials from Session 2.2, p. 65 **2C** • Materials from Session 2.4, p. 76 **2D** • Materials from Session 2.3, p. 71
③ DISCUSSION **Checking In**	5 MIN	CLASS	
④ SESSION FOLLOW-UP **Practice**			• *Student Math Handbook Flip Chart,* pp. 11–12

*See *Materials to Prepare*, p. 57.

Classroom Routines

Calendar: How Many Days . . . ? Students use the calendar to determine how many days since a class event or holiday that happened this month. Discuss students' strategies for determining the number of days.

ACTIVITY 1
Quick Images: Ten-Frames

10–15 MIN   CLASS

In *Quick Images: Ten-Frames,* students briefly see an image of dots arranged in a Ten-Frame and then try to use pennies to reproduce the quantity on their own Ten-Frame.

Students need to be seated so that they can see the image when it is shown, and each student needs a blank Ten-Frame and ten pennies.

Today we're going to do an activity called Quick Images. We'll be looking at some images, or pictures, of dots arranged in a Ten-Frame. It's called Quick Images because you'll get to see the picture for only a short time. Then I'll cover it up, and your job is to try to show what you saw with the pennies and your Ten-Frame. Let's do one together so that you can see how it works.

Find the transparent image of two dots in a Ten-Frame.

Before turning on the overhead projector, explain where the dot image will appear and remind students to look carefully because they will not have long to get the picture in their mind. To help students concentrate on the image, they should not try to use the pennies to make the image while the image is visible.

Hands in your laps. Right now you are just going to look at the image. You will try to make it afterwards.

Show the image for a little longer than five seconds for this first time, and then cover it. (Usually the image will be shown for about five seconds.) ❷

Now, put pennies on your Ten-Frame to show what you saw.

If some students are concerned that they cannot recall the figure exactly, assure them that they will have another chance to see the picture and revise their work.

When students have completed their first attempts at representing the image, explain that you are going to show it again. Encourage students to study the picture carefully while it is visible.

Keep your hands in your laps. Here comes the picture again. Look carefully!

Show the image for another five seconds. Then students revise their arrangement of pennies.

When students are finished, show the image while you ask students to explain how they remembered what they saw.

Teaching Notes

❶ **Alternatives to an Overhead** If you do not have an overhead projector, use copies you have enlarged on the copier, or sketch the images on large paper and turn the paper over to hide it from view.

❷ **How Long?** You may need to adjust the amount of time you flash the image. If you show the image for too long, students will simply copy the image from the screen, rather than building from their mental image. If you show it too briefly, they will not have time to form a mental image and will not be sure what to draw or build.

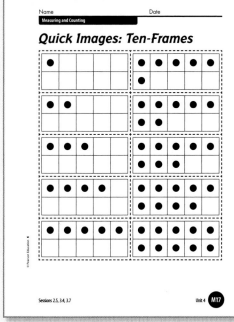

▲ **Resource Masters, M17**

When you first saw the dots in the Ten-Frame, what did you remember that helped you make your own copy of the image?

Reassure students that it can be difficult to tell the number of dots. Also reassure students that they will have other opportunities to do *Quick Images*, so that they will have time to practice and continue to get better at this.

Repeat the activity another time or two, using the images that show 3 and then 6 dots.

The teacher shows an image of dots on a Ten-Frame for five seconds.

Follow these steps each time:

- Show the image for about five seconds.
- Students use pennies to make a copy of the image on their Ten-Frame.
- Show the image again briefly.
- Students revise their work.
- With the image showing, volunteers share how many dots they saw and how they remembered.

MATH WORKSHOP

15–25 MIN

2 Counting Activities

The following four activities are available during Math Workshop. Explain what is in the Counting Jar and briefly review the way this routine works in your class. Also explain that *Collect 15 Together* is the same as *Collect 10 Together,* except that the goal is to collect 15 pennies instead of 10. Remind students what materials are required for each activity and where they are located.

Both of the new Math Workshop activities provide practice with counting amounts to 15. Given that students are expected to be able to count a set of 15 objects accurately (Benchmark 2) by the end of this unit, and that they have spent several sessions working on counting activities, this is a good place to look closely at students' strategies for counting. Use Assessment Checklist: Counting (M15) to keep track of your observations.

Professional Development

 Teacher Notes: Counting Is More Than 1, 2, 3, p. 170 and Observing Kindergarteners as They Count, p. 171

2A Counting Jar

INDIVIDUALS

Students count the objects in the Counting Jar—a set of 15 objects. Then they create an equivalent set and find a way to record what they found out.

ONGOING ASSESSMENT: Observing Students at Work

See Session 1.2, page 36, for what to observe.

DIFFERENTIATION: Supporting the Range of Learners

Intervention Some students may have difficulty counting a set of objects this size. They may not know the sequence of numbers above 10 or may have difficulty keeping track of so many objects. In the first case, count together with students on the number line and then count the cubes together. In the latter, demonstrate touching each cube as you count it or moving each cube to an "already counted" pile as they count it.

2B *Collect 15 Together*

PAIRS

This activity is the same as *Collect 10 Together* (for complete details, see Session 2.2, page 66), except that students collect 15 pennies instead of 10.

DIFFERENTIATION: Supporting the Range of Learners

Intervention Students who are having difficulty counting and comparing amounts to 15 should continue to play *Collect 10*.

2C *Roll and Record 2*

PAIRS

For complete details about this activity, see Session 2.4, page 77.

DIFFERENTIATION: Supporting the Range of Learners

Extension Students who are counting on or using combinations they know to figure out their total may be ready to play with a 1–6 number cube and a 1–3 dot cube.

2D *Build On*

PAIRS

For complete details about this activity, see Session 2.3, page 72.

DISCUSSION

Checking In

5 MIN **CLASS**

Take this opportunity to discuss any difficulties that you noticed while observing students at work. The topic may be mathematical in nature, such as a strategy you would like all students to consider (e.g., using the number line to help count or write numbers) or a common error or misconception you would like students to discuss (e.g., saying the wrong name for numbers in the teens).

Other alternatives include checking in with students about which activities they have been choosing, asking everyone to hold up a piece of work, or allowing students to raise a question or make a comment about today's math class.

SESSION FOLLOW-UP

4 Practice

Student Math Handbook Flip Chart: Use the *Student Math Handbook Flip Chart* pages 11–12 to reinforce concepts from today's session. See pages 186–190 in the back of this unit.

Mathematical Emphases

Counting and Quantity Developing strategies for accurately counting a set of objects by ones

Math Focus Points

◆ Counting spaces and moving on a gameboard

◆ Creating a set of a given size

Whole Number Operations Making sense of and developing strategies to solve addition and subtraction problems with small numbers

Math Focus Points

◆ Modeling the action of combining and separating situations

◆ Combining two amounts

◆ Separating one amount from another

◆ Adding or subtracting one to/from numbers up to 10

◆ Adding to or subtracting from one quantity to make another quantity

Counting and Quantity Developing an understanding of the magnitude and position of numbers

Math Focus Points

◆ Developing an understanding of more than and fewer than

◆ Comparing two quantities to determine which is more

Whole Number Operations Using manipulatives, drawings, tools, and notation to show strategies and solutions

Math Focus Points

◆ Using a Ten-Frame to develop visual images of quantities up to 10

This Investigation also focuses on

◆ Thinking strategically about moves on a gameboard

Changing Quantities: How Many Now?

	Student Activity Book	Student Math Handbook Flip Chart	Professional Development: Read Ahead of Time	
SESSION 3.1 p. 90				
Racing Bears Students learn, play, and discuss *Racing Bears,* a game that involves rolling a dot cube to move teddy bear counters along four tracks of 10. The object is to land each bear on the tenth space in order to collect a counter. The game is over when players have collected 10 counters.	34			
SESSION 3.2 p. 95				
Story Problems Students act out story problems about combining and separating and discuss ways to solve them. Math Workshop focuses on counting and finding the total after a small amount is added.		31–34	• **Teacher Notes:** Creating Your Own Story Problems, p. 172; Story Problems in Kindergarten, p. 174 • **Dialogue Box:** How Many Fish in All?, p. 182; How Are These Stories Different?, p. 183	
SESSION 3.3 p. 100				
One More, One Fewer Students learn how to play *One More, One Fewer,* a game that asks students to figure out what is one more or one fewer, than a given number. Math Workshop focuses on counting and on finding the total after a small amount is added or taken away. The session ends with students acting out and solving several story problems.	35	25, 26, 31–34	• **Teacher Note:** Assessing *One More, One Fewer*, p. 176	

Classroom Routines See page 20 for an overview.

Today's Question	Patterns on the Pocket Chart
• Today's Question charts for Sessions 3.1 and 3.5. See instructions on pages 90 and 109.	• Pocket Chart(s) or Sentence Pocket Chart
Attendance	• Question Mark Cards (from Investigation 1)
• No materials needed	• Pattern Blocks (6 of each color)
Calendar	• Prepared cups or baggies of pattern blocks (1 per pair)
• Monthly calendar	

Materials to Gather	Materials to Prepare
• **1-to-3 dot cubes** (1 per pair; from Session 2.2) • **Teddy bear (or other) counters** (4 per pair) • **Additional small counters such as buttons, beads, or pennies** (4 per pair)	• **M19–M20, Family Letter** Make copies. (1 per student) • **M18, *Racing Bears* Gameboard** Make copies. (as needed)
• **Materials for *Racing Bears*** See Session 3.1. • **Materials for Counting Jar** See Session 2.5. • **Materials for *Collect 15 Together*** See Sessions 2.2 and 2.5. • **Materials for *Roll and Record 2*** See Session 2.4.	
• **Primary Number Cards** (1 deck per pair, with 10 and Wild Cards removed) • **Pennies or other counters** (15–20 per pair) • **Materials for *Racing Bears*** See Session 3.1. • **Materials for Counting Jar** See Session 2.5. • **Materials for *Collect 15 Together*** See Sessions 2.2 and 2.5. • **Materials for *Roll and Record 2*** See Session 2.4.	• **M13, Ten-Frame** Make copies. (as needed) • **M21, *One More, One Fewer*** Make copies. (as needed) • **M22, Assessment Checklist: *One More, One Fewer*** ☑ Make copies. (3–4 per class) • **Plus or Minus 1 Cubes** Label three stick-on dots with "+1" and three with "−1" and use them to cover the faces of a cube. (1 per pair)

☑ Checklist Available

Changing Quantities: How Many Now?, *continued*

SESSION 3.4 p. 104	Student Activity Book	Student Math Handbook Flip Chart	Professional Development: Read Ahead of Time	
Double Compare Students learn how to play *Double Compare,* a card game in which players turn over two cards and then compare their totals to see which is larger. Math Workshop continues to focus on counting and on finding the total after a small amount is added or taken away. The session ends with a round of *Quick Images* of dots arranged in a Ten-Frame.	36		• **Teacher Note:** *Double Compare:* Strategies for Comparing and Combining, p. 178	
SESSION 3.5 p. 109				
More or Less at the End? Math Workshop continues to focus on counting and on finding a total after a small amount is added or taken away. Class discussion focuses on story problems, with students thinking about whether different situations result in more or fewer and whether those situations are about combining or separating.		21, 22, 31–34		
SESSION 3.6 p. 113				
Build It/Change It Students learn how to play *Build It/ Change It,* a game that asks players to figure out how to change one quantity into another. Math Workshop also focuses on combining and comparing and on finding the total after one is added or taken away.	30	21, 22		
SESSION 3.7 p. 117				
Who Has More? Class begins with several *Quick Images* of dots arranged in a Ten-Frame. Math Workshop focuses on changing one quantity into another, combining and comparing, and on finding the total after one is added or taken away. Class discussion focuses on how students know who has more when they play *Double Compare.*		21, 22, 25, 26	• **Teacher Note:** *Double Compare:* Strategies for Comparing and Combining, p. 178	

Materials to Gather	Materials to Prepare
• **Primary Number Cards** (1 deck per pair, with 7–10 and Wild Cards removed) • **Transparency,** *Quick Images: Ten-Frames* (from Investigation 2) • **Connecting cubes, pennies or other counters** (25 per pair) • **Materials for** *One More, One Fewer* See Session 3.3. • **Materials for** *Racing Bears* See Session 3.1. • **Materials for** *Collect 15 Together* See Session 3.2.	• **M13, Ten-Frame** Make copies. (as needed)
• **Pennies or other counters** (15–20 per student) • **Materials for** *Double Compare* See Session 3.4. • **Materials for** *One More, One Fewer* See Session 3.3. • **Materials for** *Racing Bears* See Session 3.1. • **Materials for** *Collect 15 Together* See Session 2.2.	
• **Primary Number Cards** (1 deck per pair, with Wild Cards removed) • **Pennies or other counters** (15–20 per pair) • **Materials for** *Double Compare* See Session 3.4. • **Materials for** *One More, One Fewer* See Session 3.3.	• **M13, Ten-Frame** Make copies. (as needed)
• **Transparency,** *Quick Images: Ten-Frames* (from Investigation 2) • **Pennies or other counters** (15–20 per student) • **Primary Number Cards** • **Connecting cubes or counters** • **Materials for** *Build It/Change It* See Session 3.6. • **Materials for** *Double Compare* See Session 3.4. • **Materials for** *One More, One Fewer* See Session 3.3.	• **M13, Ten-Frame** Make copies. (as needed)

Racing Bears

Math Focus Points

- Counting spaces and moving on a gameboard
- Thinking strategically about moves on a gameboard

Today's Plan		Materials
ACTIVITY **① Introducing *Racing Bears***	5–10 MIN CLASS	• *Student Activity Book,* p. 34 • One 1-to-3 dot cube; teddy bear (or other) counters; additional small counters such as buttons, beads, or pennies
ACTIVITY **② Racing Bears**	20–25 MIN PAIRS	• *Student Activity Book,* p. 34 • M18* • 1-to-3 dot cubes; teddy bear (or other) counters; other small counters such as buttons, beads, or pennies
DISCUSSION **③ Racing Bears**	5–10 MIN CLASS	• *Student Activity Book,* p. 34 • Materials from Activity 2
SESSION FOLLOW-UP **④ Homework**		• M19–M20, Family Letter*

*See *Materials to Prepare,* p. 87.

Classroom Routines

Today's Question: Do You Like to Drink Milk? On chart paper, create a 2-row, *horizontal* table titled "Do you like to drink milk?" with the heading "Yes" written at the left of one row and "No" at the left of the other row. Students respond by writing their names in the appropriate row. Count the responses as a class and discuss what the results of the survey tell you.

ACTIVITY

1 Introducing *Racing Bears*

5–10 MIN CLASS

Explain to students that they will be learning a new game called *Racing Bears*. Show them how to set up the gameboard. Place a teddy bear counter at the beginning of each of the four tracks shown on *Student Activity Book* page 34 or *Racing Bears* Gameboard (M18) and a counter such as a button in the circle at the end of each track.

You and your partner will be working together to collect ten [buttons] in all. When a bear lands on a [button], you and your partner get to take that [button] and keep it.

Play a demonstration game with a volunteer to explain the rules.

I am going to play a few rounds with [Sarah] so we can learn how to play. [Sarah] can roll the cube first. [Sarah rolls the cube.] What did she roll? . . . How many spaces can she move? . . . How do you know?

Students might say:

"The cube shows 3, so that's how many spaces she can move."

[Sarah], please choose a bear and move it [3] spaces.

Now I get a chance to roll the cube. . . . What did I roll? How many spaces can I move? I can choose to move any bear on the track. I can move the one that [Sarah] just moved, or I can choose a different bear to move.

Choose a bear and move that number of spaces. Continue taking turns. As one or more of the bears nears the end of its track, ask students to decide which bear to move in order to land on a counter.

[Sarah] just rolled a [#]. Remember that our goal is to land on a [button] so that we can collect it. Look carefully at our game board. Which bear do you think we should move? Is there a bear we could move that would let us capture a button?

Explain that when a counter is captured or collected, players should put the bear back at the beginning of the track and place a new counter in the circle.

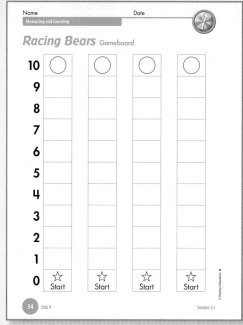

▲ Student Activity Book, p. 34;
Resource Masters, M18

Note that players can split a roll, and move more than one bear in a turn. For example, if a player rolls a 3 and the red bear is on the eighth space of its track, the player can move the red bear two spaces to get a counter, and then move another bear one additional space. If this situation does not arise naturally, use one of your turns to demonstrate what happens when you roll a number that would take a particular bear past the tenth space.

I rolled a [3], but I want to move the red bear, which is [2] spaces from the end. [Move the red bear the two spaces.] I rolled [3], and I moved [2]. How many moves do I have left? How do you know?

You may need to demonstrate this type of move several times before students get used to the idea of splitting a roll.

Play several rounds, asking students to explain how they figured out how many spaces to move, how they decided which bear to move, and how they counted the spaces moved. Remind students that the game is over when the pair playing has collected at least 10 counters.

ACTIVITY

20–25 MIN **CLASS**

❷ *Racing Bears*

Pairs take turns rolling a dot cube to move teddy bear counters along four tracks of ten. The goal is to land on, and thereby capture, the counters on the tenth spaces. The game is over when players have together collected ten counters.❶

A student moves a bear the number of spaces that match a number rolled on the dot cube.

ONGOING ASSESSMENT: Observing Students at Work

Students determine the number of dots on a dot cube and then move that number of spaces on one or more tracks on a gameboard.

- **Do students recognize the dot patterns?** Or, do they count the dots to determine the number of spaces to move?

- **Do they move the correct number of spaces?** Do they say one and only one number for each space as they move along the track?

- **How do students choose which bear to move?** Do they review their options? How do they figure out how many more spaces a bear has to go to land on 10?

- **How do students handle rolls that would take a bear past ten?**

DIFFERENTIATION: Supporting the Range of Learners

Intervention Some students make mistakes as they move the bears along the tracks. Some say "1" for the space the bear is on (rather than as they move the bear one square forward). Others roll a 3 and move a bear to the space numbered 3 instead of moving a bear forward 3 spaces. These students may benefit from playing in a small group with you. As you play, ask:

- Suppose that I rolled a 3 and I want to move this bear. Do I count the space the bear is on? Why?

- I rolled a 3. What do I do with this bear? Do I move it to the space with the number 3 next to it?

If you notice many students making these types of errors, make these questions the focus of a Checking In discussion.

Intervention Some students may have difficulty with rolls that take a bear past the tenth space. For these students, adjust the rules such that when a bear reaches the tenth space, it means the end of a turn, whether or not there are leftovers from the roll.

Teaching Note

② **Nonmathematical Reasons** Some students suggest moving a bear because it is their favorite color or favorite bear. Encourage students to think mathematically and strategically by asking whether this will help them collect as many counters as possible.

DISCUSSION

③ Racing Bears

5–10 MIN   CLASS

Math Focus Points for Discussion

◆ Thinking strategically about moves on a gameboard

Set up a sample game with bears at various locations on the tracks. Place one or two bears close to the end of a track and one or two more toward the beginning. Gather students so that they can see the game board.

Suppose that I was in the middle of playing Racing Bears with [Raul] and that this is where all the bears were. Remember we are trying to collect as many buttons as we can.

Roll the dot cube.

I rolled a [3]. Which bear do you think I should move? . . . Why do you think so? **②**

Some students will suggest moving a bear that is close to the end of one track in order to get it closer to the end. Others will notice when a bear is exactly the amount you rolled away from a counter and suggest moving that bear so that you can collect it. Still others see when they can split up a roll and suggest moving more than one bear in order to collect one or more counters.

Try each strategy that students suggest as you continue to play the sample game with the class. Encourage students to think strategically by asking each time whether the move will help them collect as many counters as possible.

SESSION FOLLOW-UP

④ Homework

Family Letter: Send home copies of the Family Letter (M19–M20).

Story Problems

Math Focus Points

◆ Modeling the action of combining and separating situations

◆ Combining two amounts

◆ Separating one amount from another

Today's Plan		Materials
ACTIVITY ① **Three Story Problems** 🕐 10–15 MIN 👥 CLASS		

MATH WORKSHOP
② **Counting and Combining**   🕐 15–25 MIN
   ② Ⓐ *Racing Bears*
   ② Ⓑ *Counting Jar*
   ② Ⓒ *Collect 15 Together*
   ② Ⓓ *Roll and Record 2*
		②Ⓐ • Materials from Session 3.1, p. 90
		②Ⓑ • Materials from Session 2.5, p. 80
		②Ⓒ • Materials from Session 2.2, p. 65
		②Ⓓ • Materials from Session 2.4, p. 76

DISCUSSION ③ **Checking In** 🕐 5 MIN 👥 CLASS		
SESSION FOLLOW-UP ④ **Practice**		• *Student Math Handbook Flip Chart,* pp. 31–34

Classroom Routines

Patterns on the Pocket Chart: What Comes Next? Arrange an AAB repeating pattern on the pocket chart, using 10 pattern blocks (orange square, orange square, blue rhombus). Follow the basic *Patterns* activity. Students hold up the block that they think is under each Question Mark Card.

Teaching Notes

❶ Choosing Appropriate Problems It is important to choose problems that your students can easily visualize and act out. If the context of a story is unfamiliar, choose another, but keep the numbers the same.

❻ What's the Answer? Some students anticipate a question at the end, such as "How many fish in all did I see?" and are eager to answer it. Explain that, right now you are interested in what students remember about the story, and that later you will be figuring out how many fish there are in all.

Professional Development

❷ Teacher Note: Creating Your Own Story Problems, p. 172

❹ Teacher Note: Story Problems in Kindergarten, p. 174

Math Note

❸ Presenting Story Problems The story problems in this unit are presented in a way that encourages students to think about, visualize, and make sense of the action in a problem.

Differentiation

❺ English Language Learners Word problems present special challenges for English Language Learners, who may understand the underlying math concepts but not the language of the problem. If English Language Learners cannot easily follow the story problems, meet with a small group and review the problems together, using real-life objects, manipulatives, or simple drawings to represent the things that are added or subtracted in each story.

ACTIVITY

① Three Story Problems

10-15 MIN   CLASS

I'm going to tell you a story.❶ ❷ As you listen, picture the story in your mind. If it helps you concentrate, close your eyes.❸ ❹

For students who are not proficient in English, draw quick sketches of important words on the board to aid in comprehension.❺

Here's a story about some fish: Three little fish were swimming in the clear, cold water of a pond. Then three more little fish came swimming up to join them. . . . Now, who can tell me what happened in the story? What happened first?

Students might say:

"There were fish swimming in a pond."

How many fish were swimming? *(Three)* Did anything else happen?

Students might say:

"The three new fish came to swim with the other fish."

Ask several students to tell what they remember about the story: Even if one student tells the story correctly, ask a few more students to tell it as well.❻

When the group is clear about the story, have the class act it out. Choose three students to be the three fish that swim in the pond first. Give them a moment to act out their roles as fish, and then reread the story and call up three more students to join the first three.

There were three fish in the pond, and then three more fish joined them. How could we figure out how many fish in all were in the pond?

Although some students may be eager to give an answer, keep the emphasis on solution strategies, such as counting the students who acted as fish, counting on their fingers, or "just knowing" that three and three is six.❼

Follow the same process with another combining story.

Let's listen to another story. Five bees were buzzing around a flower. Two more bees were at the hive. They flew over to join the others at the flower.

Ask a few students to put the story in their own words, and call up volunteers to act it out. Ask how to find the total number of bees at the flower and try out one or two of their strategies as a group.

Next, tell a related story that involves separating one amount from another. At this point, do not mention that the story will be different from the others in any way. The goal is for students to think about the action in the story and choose a strategy that reflects that action.

I'm going to tell another story about bees. Again, picture the story in your mind. There were seven bees buzzing around the flower. Two bees left the flower and flew back to the hive.

Again, have several students restate the problem in their own words to make sure that they have an understanding of the situation. Then, have students act it out to illustrate the action that is taking place. After students have put the story in their own words and acted it out, ask this question:

How could we tell how many bees were left at the flower?

Students may suggest counting the number of student-bees remaining at the flower or counting back two from seven. Some kindergarteners may "just know" some addition pairs, but they are less likely to be familiar with subtraction pairs, such as $7 - 2 = 5$, and will probably not suggest such an approach. If any students suggest combining the two amounts (7 and 2), ask them to retell the story and to watch closely while it is acted out again.

If no one mentions how the two bee stories are similar or different, raise these questions yourself.

How were these two stories similar? What was the same about them? How were they different?

When students think about the similarities of these problems, they talk about the characters (bees, student actors), the context (flowers and a hive), and possibly the numbers involved (5, 2, and 7).

Professional Development

❼ **Dialogue Box:** How Many Fish in All?, p. 182

⑧ **Dialogue Box:** How Are These Stories Different?, p. 183

Math Notes

⑨ **Key Words** In order for students to solve story problems, they must make sense of the actions involved. Encourage students to think about whether the quantities are being combined or separated and to use their own language to describe those actions. Using a "key words" approach—such as looking for words such as "altogether" and "left" as clues—can have the opposite effect, disconnecting students from the process of trying to make sense of the situation as a whole.

⑩ **Building a Foundation** As they gain experience visualizing and modeling the action of a variety of addition and subtraction problems, students will be able to tackle problems that involve larger numbers and more complex structures—problems that they may not always be able to act out easily. They will also learn to consider relationships among the quantities in a story.

In discussing the differences between these two stories, the focus should be on the action. In the first story, two groups of bees came together, but in the second, some of the bees flew away; in the first story, there were more bees at the flower at the end, and in the second story, there were fewer.⑧ ⑨ ⑩

MATH WORKSHOP

② Counting and Combining

15–25 MIN

Explain that the following four activities are available during Math Workshop. Remind students what each activity entails, what materials are required, and where they are located.

2A *Racing Bears*

PAIRS

For complete details about this activity, see Session 3.1, page 91.

DIFFERENTIATION: Supporting the Range of Learners

Extension If some students are easily determining the number of dots on the number cube and quickly moving the bears on the board, ask questions that encourage them to play more strategically, perhaps splitting rolls to capture two chips instead of one.

2B *Counting Jar*

INDIVIDUALS

For complete details about this activity, see Session 2.5, page 83.

2C *Collect 15 Together*

PAIRS

For complete details about this activity, see Session 2.2, page 66 and Session 2.5, page 83.

2D *Roll and Record 2*

PAIRS

For complete details about this activity, see Session 2.4, page 77.

DISCUSSION
③ Checking In

Take this opportunity to discuss any difficulties that you noticed while observing students at work. The topic may be mathematical in nature, such as a strategy you would like all students to consider (e.g., ways to split up moves in *Racing Bears*) or a common error or misconception you would like students to discuss (e.g., counting the space a bear is on or moving a bear to the space labeled with the number rolled, rather than moving it that many spaces). The issue might also be management related (e.g., playing cooperatively).

Other alternatives include checking in with students about which activities they have been choosing (e.g., "Who has had a chance to play *Racing Bears* a second time?"), asking everyone to hold up a piece of work, or allowing students to raise a question or make a comment about today's math class.

SESSION FOLLOW-UP
④ Practice

Student Math Handbook Flip Chart: Use the *Student Math Handbook Flip Chart* pages 31–34 to reinforce concepts from today's session. See pages 186–190 in the back of this unit.

One More, One Fewer

2 days

Math Focus Points

◆ Developing an understanding of more than and fewer than

◆ Adding or subtracting one to/from numbers up to 10

◆ Modeling the action of combining and separating situations

Vocabulary

more	minus
fewer	add
plus	remove

Today's Plan

	Materials
ACTIVITY **①** **Introducing *One More, One Fewer*** 🕐 5–10 MIN 👥 CLASS	• M13*; M21* • Primary Number Cards; Pennies or other counters; Plus/Minus 1 Cube*
MATH WORKSHOP **②** **Counting, Combining, and Adding/Subtracting 1** 🕐 15–25 MIN **2A** *One More, One Fewer* **2B** *Racing Bears* **2C** *Counting Jar* **2D** *Collect 15 Together* **2E** *Roll and Record 2*	• *Student Activity Book*, p. 35 **2A** • M13*; M21*; M22* ✓ • Materials from Activity 1 **2B** • Materials from Session 3.1, p. 90 **2C** • Materials from Session 2.5, p. 80 **2D** • Materials from Session 2.2, p. 65 **2E** • Materials from Session 2.4, p. 76
ACTIVITY **③** **Acting out Story Problems** 🕐 10 MIN 👥 CLASS	
SESSION FOLLOW-UP **④** **Practice**	• *Student Math Handbook Flip Chart*, pp. 25, 26, 31–34

*See *Materials to Prepare*, p. 87.

Classroom Routines

Attendance: How Many Have Counted? Count around the circle as usual but pause several times during the count to ask students how many people have counted so far and how they know. Help students see why the number they say represents the number of students who have counted so far and that the last number represents the total number of students in class today.

ACTIVITY

1 Introducing *One More, One Fewer*

5–10 MIN CLASS

Today we are going to learn a new game. It's called *One More, One Fewer*. What does the word more mean? . . . What about fewer?

As you talk about these words, show students a Plus or Minus 1 cube, and discuss how these words relate to what's on the cube (+1 = one more, −1 = one fewer). ❶

Explain that each pair of students needs a deck of Primary Number Cards, a Plus or Minus 1 cube, a set of pennies, a Ten-Frame (M13) and *Student Activity Book* page 35.

Then, play a few rounds to introduce the game to the class. Ask a volunteer to turn over one of his or her cards.

[Kyle] turned over one of his cards and it had a 6 on it so he puts 6 pennies on his Ten-Frame. [Kyle 's] partner writes that number on the recording sheet.

Now [Kyle] rolls the cube to decide if he needs to figure out what is one more than 6, or if he needs to figure out what is one fewer than 6. What does the cube say that [Kyle] should do?

Depending on the roll, Player 1 either takes a penny off or adds a penny to their Ten-Frame. Player 2 circles +1 or −1 on *One More, One Fewer* (M21).

Together the students determine their new total, and Player 2 records it. Then, the players switch roles.

Now [Corey] and [Jack] switch roles. This time [Corey] turns over a card and counts that many pennies onto the Ten-Frame, and rolls the Plus or Minus 1 cube to see whether [she] needs to add or remove. [Jack] is the recorder.

Play several rounds so that students get experience with rolling +1 and −1.

MATH WORKSHOP

2 Counting, Combining, and Adding/Subtracting 1

15–25 MIN

Explain that the following five activities are available during Math Workshop, and that today is the last day that the Counting Jar will be available. Remind students what each activity entails, what materials are required, and where they are located.

One More, One Fewer

Starting Number	+1 or −1	Ending Total
	+1	
	−1	
	+1	
	−1	
	+1	
	−1	
	+1	
	−1	
	+1	
	−1	
	+1	
	−1	
	+1	
	−1	

▲ **Student Activity Book, p. 35;
Resource Masters, M21**

❷ᴬ *One More, One Fewer*

PAIRS

Students pick a number card and then roll a cube to determine whether they should add or subtract one to or from that number. They work on a Ten-Frame (*Student Activity Book* page 30 or M13) and record their work on *Student Activity Book* page 35 or *One More, One Fewer* (M21).

ONGOING ASSESSMENT: Observing Students at Work

Students find the total after one is added to, or subtracted from, a set of objects.❷ ❸

- **How do students determine the number on the card?** Do they "just know" the name of the number? Do they count the objects on the card? Do they accurately place that many pennies on their Ten-Frame?

- **How do students determine the total after adding or subtracting one?** Do they count all of the pennies, starting from 1? Do they count on or back, saying, "It was 6 and one more is 7"?

DIFFERENTIATION: Supporting the Range of Learners

Intervention Students who have difficulty creating an equivalent set of pennies on the Ten-Frame need more practice with *Build It* and *Build On*.

Assessment Checklist: One More, One Fewer

Student	Figures out one more than a number	Figures out one less than a number

Lisa	✓ one more, one fewer
	  just knows
		✓ counts back
		  one more, one fewer

Emma	one more, one fewer counts from 1	counts from 1 one more, one fewer
Brad	collect 15 just know for #s under 3 counts from 1 for #s over 3	
Lionel	story problem counts from 1 one more, one fewer — just knows	

2B Racing Bears

PAIRS

For complete details on this activity, see Session 3.1, page 91.

2C Counting Jar

INDIVIDUALS

For complete details on this activity, see Session 2.5, page 83.

2D Collect 15 Together

PAIRS

For complete details on this activity, see Session 2.2, page 66 and Session 2.5, page 83.

2E Roll and Record 2

PAIRS

For complete details on this activity, see Session 2.4, page 77.

ACTIVITY

10 MIN   CLASS

3 Acting out Story Problems

As you did in Session 3.2, tell a story that involves either combining or separating and ask one or two students to put the story in their own words. Then ask volunteers to act out the story. Pose a problem about the story and gather solution strategies. Do not tell students beforehand whether the story involves combining or separating.❹

Consider telling two related stories, one that involves adding one and another that involves subtracting one. For example:

Five children were playing on the jungle gym. Then another child came and joined them. How many children were playing on the jungle gym?

Six children were playing on the jungle gym. Then one left to play on the swings. How many children were playing on the jungle gym?

SESSION FOLLOW-UP

4 Practice

Student Math Handbook Flip Chart: Use the *Student Math Handbook Flip Chart* pages 25–26, 31–34 to reinforce concepts from today's session. See pages 186–190 in the back of this unit.

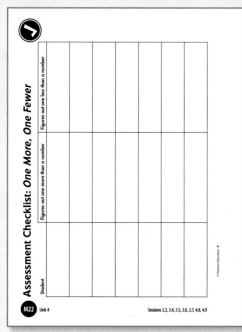

▲ Resource Masters, M22 ☑

Assessment Checklist: One More, One Fewer

Figures out one less than a number

Figures out one more than a number

Student

© Pearson Education K

M22 Unit 4

Sessions 3.3, 3.4, 3.5, 3.6, 3.7, 4.8, 4.9

Professional Development

❹ **Teacher Note:** Creating Your Own Story Problems, p. 172 and Story Problems in Kindergarten, p. 174

Double Compare

Math Focus Points

◆ Combining two amounts

◆ Comparing two quantities to determine which is more

◆ Using a Ten-Frame to develop visual images of quantities up to 10

Vocabulary

compare
larger
total

Today's Plan			Materials
ACTIVITY **①** **Introducing *Double Compare***	🕐 5–10 MIN	👥 CLASS	• Primary Number Cards (with 7–10 and Wild Cards removed) • Connecting cubes or other counters
MATH WORKSHOP **②** **Counting, Combining, and Comparing** **2A** *Double Compare* **2B** *One More, One Fewer* **2C** *Racing Bears* **2D** *Collect 15 Together*	🕐 15–25 MIN		**2A** • Materials from Activity 1 **2B** • Materials from Session 3.3, p. 100 **2C** • Materials from Session 3.1, p. 90 **2D** • Materials from Session 2.2, p. 65
ACTIVITY **③** **Quick Images: Ten-Frames**	🕐 10 MIN	👥 CLASS	• M13* • Transparency, *Quick Images: Ten-Frames* (from Investigation 2) • Pennies or other counters
SESSION FOLLOW-UP **④** **Practice**			• *Student Activity Book*, p. 36

*See *Materials to Prepare*, p. 89.

Classroom Routines

Calendar: Mixed Up Calendar Change the position of two numbers (1 to 10) on the calendar so that they are out of order. Challenge students to find the mistakes and help you fix them.

ACTIVITY
1 Introducing *Double Compare*

5–10 MIN   CLASS

Professional Development

🛈 **Teacher Note:** *Double Compare:* Strategies for Comparing and Combining, p. 178

Explain to students that *Double Compare* is similar to the card game *Compare,* which they already know how to play.

In this game each player turns over two cards. Then you compare the total of your cards with the total of your partner's cards. The player with the larger total says "Me."

Enlist two student volunteers to play a demonstration game, or choose a student to play with you. Have counters available for students to figure out or compare the totals.

[Cindy] turned over a 2 and a 5. [Brad] turned over a 5 and a 5. Who has more? How do you know?

Students might say:

"[Brad] has more. I counted the pictures."

"[Brad] has more because 5 and 5 is more than 5 and 2."

Did anyone think about it in a different way?

Expect students to answer with a range of strategies.🛈

Explain to students that any time players have the same total, they turn over the next two cards and compare those totals. The game is over when players have turned over all their cards.

MATH WORKSHOP
2 Counting, Combining, and Comparing

15–25 MIN

Explain that the following four activities are available during Math Workshop. Remind students what each activity entails, what materials are required, and where they are located.

2A Double Compare

PAIRS

Each player turns over two cards. Then, players decide which pair of cards shows the larger total. ❷

Students determine who has the greater total on their cards.

ONGOING ASSESSMENT: Observing Students at Work

Students combine and compare numbers up to 12.

- **Do students recognize the numbers on the cards?** Do they count the pictures to determine the number? Can they count the pictures accurately?

- **Do students combine the two quantities?** How? Do they count them all? Do they count up from one of the numbers? Do they "just know" any of the sums? Which ones?

- **How do students determine which total is larger?** Do they "just know"? Do they count the objects pictured on the card? Do they use counters? Do any students reason about which total is larger without actually finding the total (for example, "I got a 2 and a 4, and you got a 5 and a 4. Yours is more because the 4s are the same and 5 is bigger than 2")? ❸

DIFFERENTIATION: Supporting the Range of Learners

Intervention For some students, counting the pictures on the cards is challenging. Encourage them to use cubes or counters to create sets that match the cards. Then, they can count the cubes to find the total.

Similarly, students who are having difficulty comparing quantities can build and compare cube towers.

Extension If students are able to determine who says "me" without counting the totals, ask them to explain their thinking. Ask what is special about the cards that allows them to do that and whether they think that strategy would work with other numbers.

2B One More, One Fewer

PAIRS

For complete details about this activity, see Session 3.3, page 101.

DIFFERENTIATION: Supporting the Range of Learners

Extension Students who understand the concept of one more and one fewer and are ready to think more abstractly about numbers can play without the Ten-Frame. They may play on a number line or use only the Primary Number Cards. You may also change the cube, adding a +2 and a −2.

2C Racing Bears

PAIRS

For complete details about this activity, see Session 3.1, page 91.

2D Collect 15 Together

PAIRS

For complete details about this activity, see Session 2.2, page 66 and Session 2.5, page 83.

ACTIVITY

10 MIN   CLASS

3 Quick Images: Ten-Frames

Distribute a blank Ten-Frame (M13) and ten pennies to each student. Follow the regular *Quick Images* routine, using the image with ten dots.

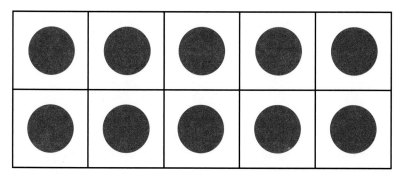

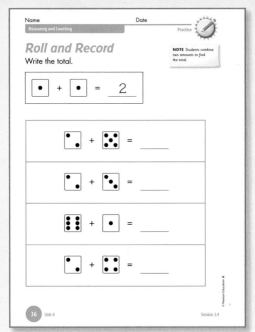

▲ Student Activity Book, p. 36

1. Flash the image for about five seconds and then cover it.

2. Give students time to build what they saw on their blank Ten-Frame.

3. Flash the image for another five seconds and then cover it.

4. Allow time for students to revise or finish their first idea.

5. Show the image a final time, and leave it showing. Students check their work and make any revisions. Students describe and discuss what helped them remember the image.

Repeat this process with the images that show eight and then nine, as time permits.

4 Practice

 Practice: For reinforcement of this unit's content, have students complete *Student Activity Book* page 36.

More or Less at the End?

Math Focus Points

- Comparing two quantities to determine which is more
- Adding or subtracting one to/from numbers up to 10
- Modeling the action of combining and separating situations

Vocabulary

combining
removing

Today's Plan		Materials
1 MATH WORKSHOP **Counting, Combining, and Comparing** **1A** *Double Compare* **1B** *One More, One Fewer* **1C** *Racing Bears* **1D** *Collect 15 Together*	20–35 MIN	**1A** • Materials from Session 3.4, p. 104 **1B** • Materials from Session 3.3, p. 100 **1C** • Materials from Session 3.1, p. 90 **1D** • Materials from Session 2.2, p. 65
2 DISCUSSION **More or Less at the End?**	10 MIN CLASS	
3 SESSION FOLLOW-UP **Practice**		• *Student Math Handbook Flip Chart,* pp. 21, 22

Classroom Routines

Today's Question: Would You Rather Take a Bath or a Shower? On chart paper, create a two-row, horizontal table titled "Would you rather take a bath or a shower?" with the label "Bath" written at the left of one row and "Shower" written at the left of the other row. Students respond by writing their names beside the appropriate label. Count the responses as a class and discuss what the results of the survey tell you.

MATH WORKSHOP

Counting, Combining, and Comparing

20–35 MIN

Explain that the following four activities are available during Math Workshop and that today is the last day *Collect 15 Together* and *Racing Bears* will be available. Remind students what each activity entails, what materials are required, and where they are located.

. . . .

1A *Double Compare*

PAIRS

For complete details on this activity, see Session 3.4, page 105.

DIFFERENTIATION: Supporting the Range of Learners

Extension Students who can quickly and accurately find the total of the two cards and decide who has more can play with a full deck of Primary Number Cards.

. . . .

1B *One More, One Fewer*

PAIRS

For complete details on this activity, see Session 3.3, page 101.

. . . .

1C *Racing Bears*

PAIRS

For complete details on this activity, see Session 3.1, page 91.

. . . .

1D *Collect 15 Together*

PAIRS

For complete details on this activity, see Session 2.2, page 66 and Session 2.5, page 83.

DISCUSSION

② More or Less at the End?

10 MIN   CLASS

Math Focus Points for Discussion

◆ Modeling the action of combining and separating situations

Gather students and pose the following story problem:

At a party [Cindy] got four balloons. Her friend gave her two more.

Before asking students to act out the story or to solve it, ask this question:

At the end of the story, will [Cindy] have more than four balloons or fewer than four balloons?

Students might say:

"More than four. In my head, I saw Cindy with four balloons and then I saw someone giving her more. So, she ends up with *more* than four balloons."

"If you have four balloons and get some more, you have more than four balloons."

As students share their ideas, keep the focus on how they know whether there are more or less balloons. Then, continue as you usually do by asking several students to retell the story, by having volunteers act it out, and then by asking the class how they would figure out how many balloons [Cindy] has now.

After they have shared their solutions and their strategies for solving the problem, ask these questions:

Was this story about putting groups together or taking a group away? How do you know?

Students might say:

"Putting groups together. Because Cindy got more balloons. No one took any of her balloons away."

Follow the same process with a story problem about separating.

There were seven leaves hanging on a tree. Three of the leaves fell off. At the end of the story are there more than seven leaves or fewer than seven leaves hanging on the tree? How do you know?

Then have students retell, act out, and solve the problem of how many leaves are on the tree. After they have shared their solutions and their strategies for solving the problem, ask these questions:

Was this story about **combining** groups or **removing** groups? How do you know?

As you continue solving story problems in this Investigation and unit, continue to ask students to think about whether there will be more or fewer at the end of the story and whether the story was about joining or combining or about removing, separating, or taking away.

SESSION FOLLOW-UP

3 Practice

Student Math Handbook Flip Chart: Use the *Student Math Handbook Flip Chart* pages 21, 22 to reinforce concepts from today's session. See pages 186–190 in the back of this unit.

Build It/Change It

Math Focus Points

◆ Creating a set of a given size

◆ Adding to or subtracting from one quantity to make another quantity

◆ Comparing two quantities to determine which is more

Today's Plan		Materials
① ACTIVITY **Introducing *Build It/Change It*** 5–10 MIN CLASS		• M13* • Primary Number Cards (with Wild Cards removed); pennies or other counters
② MATH WORKSHOP **Adding, Removing, and Comparing** 20–30 MIN **2A** *Build It/Change It* **2B** *Double Compare* **2C** *One More, One Fewer*		**2A** • *Student Activity Book,* p. 30 or M13 • Materials from Activity 1 **2B** • Materials from Session 3.4, p. 104 **2C** • Materials from Session 3.3, p. 100
③ DISCUSSION **Checking In** 5 MIN CLASS		
④ SESSION FOLLOW-UP **Practice**		• *Student Math Handbook Flip Chart,* pp. 21, 22

*See *Materials to Prepare,* p. 89.

Classroom Routines

Calendar: How Many Days . . . ? Students use the calendar to determine how many days until a class event or holiday that will happen this month. Discuss students' strategies for determining the number of days.

ACTIVITY
❶ Introducing *Build It/Change It*

5–10 MIN CLASS

Today we're going to learn a new game called *Build It/Change It*. It is similar to *Build It* and to *One More, One Fewer*.

Ask two volunteers to demonstrate a few rounds of this game. As with any of the games that involve the Primary Number Cards, partners should sit next to instead of across from each other.

To start the game, [Jennifer] turns over the top card. [Jennifer] turned over a [4], so how many counters should she place on the Ten-Frame? Now it's [Hugo's] turn. [Hugo] turns over the next card. What number did [Hugo] get? [6]

What [Hugo] needs to do is change the number of pennies on the Ten-Frame so that it matches the number on his card. How could [Hugo] change [four] pennies into [six] pennies?

Try each method that students suggest. Some clear the Ten-Frame (M13) and then place [six] on it and others add [two] pennies to the [four] that are already there.❶

Now [Jennifer] and [Hugo] change roles. [Hugo] turns over the top card and puts that many pennies on the Ten-Frame. Then [Jennifer] turns over another card and changes the pennies on the Ten-Frame to match his number.

Play a few more rounds, being sure to model a round or two that require removing some pennies from the Ten-Frame.

MATH WORKSHOP
❷ Adding, Removing, and Comparing

20–30 MIN

Explain that the following three activities are available during Math Workshop. Remind students what each activity entails, what materials are required, and where they are located.

❷A *Build It/Change It*

PAIRS

Player 1 turns over a number card and places that number of pennies on a Ten-Frame. Player 2 turns over another number card and changes the number of pennies on the Ten-Frame to match the number on the new card.

Students change the number of pennies on the Ten-Frame from matching the number on the first card turned over to matching the number on the second card turned over.

Algebra Note

❷ **Putting Some On, Taking Some Away** When they play *Build It/Change It,* some students are working with a general idea: "To change a number to a larger number, put more on. To change it to a smaller number, take some away." Encourage students who seem to be using these ideas to articulate them by asking, "How did you know to put more on instead of taking some away?"

ONGOING ASSESSMENT: Observing Students at Work

Students use counters to represent a quantity and then change it to make another quantity.

- **How do students determine the number on the card?** Do they just know the name of the number? Do they count the objects on the card?

- **Do students place the correct quantity on their Ten-Frame?**

- **How do students create a set that is equivalent to a new card?** Do they remove all the pennies and count from 1? If the new amount is more, do they count the pennies on the Ten-Frame and keep counting and adding pennies until they get to the new amount? (If the amount is fewer, do they count the pennies on the Ten-Frame until they get to the new amount?) Do they start from the number of pennies and add on (or take away) until they get to the new amount?❷

❷ᴮ *Double Compare*

For complete details about this activity, see Session 3.4, page 105.

❷ᶜ *One More, One Fewer*

For complete details about this activity, see Session 3.3, page 101.

DISCUSSION

③ Checking In

Take this opportunity to discuss any difficulties that you noticed while observing students at work. The topic may be mathematical in nature, such as a strategy you would like all students to consider (e.g., using a number's relationship to five or ten to help build a number) or a common error or misconception you would like students to discuss (e.g., placing the incorrect number of pennies in the Ten-Frame or adding on the amount on the second card turned over).

The difficulty may be logistical (e.g., turning over the top cards in *Double Compare*) or management related (e.g., working cooperatively, how much time to spend on an activity).

Other alternatives include checking in with students about which activities they have been choosing (e.g., "Thumbs up if you did *Double Compare* today. Thumbs up if you did *Build It/Change It*."), asking everyone to hold up a piece of work, or allowing students to raise a question or make a comment about today's math class.

SESSION FOLLOW-UP

④ Practice

 Student Math Handbook Flip Chart: Use the *Student Math Handbook Flip Chart* pages 21, 22 to reinforce concepts from today's session. See pages 186–190 in the back of this unit.

Who Has More?

Math Focus Points

- Using a Ten-Frame to develop visual images of quantities up to 10
- Adding to or subtracting from one quantity to make another quantity
- Comparing two quantities to determine which is more

Today's Plan		Materials
ACTIVITY **①** *Quick Images: Ten-Frames*	10 MIN · CLASS	• M13* • Transparency *Quick Images: Ten Frame* (from Investigation 2) • Pennies or other counters
MATH WORKSHOP **②** **Adding, Removing, and Comparing** **2A** *Build It/Change It* **2B** *Double Compare* **2C** *One More, One Fewer*	10–25 MIN	**2A** • Materials from Session 3.6, p. 113 **2B** • Materials from Session 3.4, p. 104 **2C** • Materials from Session 3.3, p. 100
DISCUSSION **③** **Who Has More?**	10 MIN · CLASS	• Primary Number Cards; cubes or counters
SESSION FOLLOW-UP **④** **Practice**		• *Student Math Handbook Flip Chart,* pp. 21, 22, 25, and 26

*See *Materials to Prepare,* p. 89.

Classroom Routines

Attendance: What if We Start With . . . ? As usual, count around the circle to determine the total number of students present today. Then ask students what they think would happen if the count began with a different student and why. Choose a different student to start, count again, and discuss what happens.

ACTIVITY
Quick Images: Ten-Frames

10 MIN   CLASS

Distribute a blank Ten-Frame (M13) and ten pennies to each student. Follow the *Quick Images* routine, using the image with four dots.

1. Flash the image for about five seconds and then cover it.

2. Give students time to build what they saw on their blank Ten-Frame.

3. Flash the image for another five seconds and then cover it.

4. Allow time for students to revise or finish their first idea.

5. Show the image a final time, and leave it showing. Students check their work and make any revisions. Students describe and discuss what helped them remember the image.

Repeat this process with the images that show ten and then seven, as time permits.

MATH WORKSHOP
Adding, Removing, and Comparing

10–25 MIN

Explain that the following three activities are available during Math Workshop and that today is the last day *One More, One Fewer* and *Double Compare* will be available. Remind students what each activity entails, what materials are required, and where they are located.

2A Build It/Change It
PAIRS

For complete details about this activity, see Session 3.6, page 114.

2B Double Compare
PAIRS

For complete details about this activity, see Session 3.4, page 105.

2C One More, One Fewer
PAIRS

For complete details about this activity, see Session 3.3, page 101.

③ DISCUSSION
Who Has More?

10 MIN   CLASS

Professional Development

❶ Teacher Note: *Double Compare:* Strategies for Combining and Comparing, p. 178

Math Focus Points for Discussion

◆ Comparing two quantities to determine which is more

Have students discuss their strategies for playing *Double Compare.*❶ Ask a volunteer to play a game with you.

[Lionel] and I are going to play a round of *Double Compare.* After we turn over our cards, look closely at them. See whether you can figure out who has more. I want everyone to have a chance to think about this, so please think quietly and don't call out the answer. After you decide who you think has more, [put your thumb up].

Turn over two pairs of cards and give students time to think. Have cubes available for students to use to combine or compare.

I turned over a [6] and a [4]. [Lionel] turned over a [5] and a [6]. What can we do to figure out who has more?

Students might say:

 "Build a cube tower with 6 and 4, and another with 5 and 6 and hold them next to each other to see who has more."

 "Count the pictures. See which person has more."

 "You have 6 and 4. That's 6; 7, 8, 9, 10. Lionel has 5; 6, 7, 8, 9, 10, 11. Eleven is more than 10."

 "You have 6 and Lionel has 6. Lionel has more because his other card is 5 and yours is 4 and 5 is more than 4."

Summarize each strategy that is suggested and ask the class to help you model it.

[Abby] said that she would use cubes to build a tower for each person, and then compare the towers to see which was taller. Let's try that. How many cubes do we need for my tower? How many for [Lionel's] tower?

Afterwards, ask students who used this method to raise their hands. In this way, all students' strategies are acknowledged without each individual sharing.

[Abby] built a tower for my cards and a tower for [Lionel's] cards. She saw that [Lionel's] tower was bigger, so [Lionel] had more than me. Who else used a strategy like [Abby's]?

SESSION FOLLOW-UP
Practice

Student Math Handbook Flip Chart: Use the *Student Math Handbook Flip Chart* pages 21, 22, 25, 26 to reinforce concepts from today's session. See pages 186–190 in the back of this unit.

Mathematical Emphases

Counting and Quantity Developing strategies for accurately counting a set of objects by ones

Math Focus Points

◆ Developing and analyzing visual images for quantities up to 10

◆ Creating a set of a given size

Whole Number Operations Making sense of and developing strategies to solve addition and subtraction problems with small numbers

Math Focus Points

◆ Decomposing numbers in different ways

◆ Modeling the action of combining and separating situations

◆ Exploring combinations of a number (e.g., 6 is 3 and 3 and also 5 and 1)

Whole Number Operations Using manipulatives, drawings, tools, and notation to show strategies and solutions

Math Focus Points

◆ Recording an arrangement of a quantity

◆ Using numbers to record how many

Ways to Make Numbers

	Student Activity Book	Student Math Handbook Flip Chart	Professional Development: Read Ahead of Time
SESSION 4.1 p. 128			
Six Tiles in All Students find different ways to arrange six square tiles and record one arrangement. The class looks at several examples and discusses how they might name or remember them.	37–38		• **Teacher Note:** Counting Is More Than 1, 2, 3, p. 170; Observing Kindergarteners as They Count, p. 171 • **Dialogue Box:** It Looks Like a Chair, p. 184
SESSION 4.2 p. 134			
Quick Images: Square Tiles Students see and describe an arrangement of six squares. Then the arrangement is hidden from view and students use tiles to recreate it. During Math Workshop students continue to make and record different arrangements of six tiles. The session ends with students acting out and solving several story problems.		20, 27, 28, 31–34	• **Teacher Notes:** Creating Your Own Story Problems, p. 172; Story Problems in Kindergarten, p. 174
SESSION 4.3 p. 138			
Arrangements of 5 to 10 Tiles Students make and record arrangements of square tiles for the numbers from five through ten.		20, 27	
SESSION 4.4 p. 143			
Toss the Chips Students learn, play, and discuss a new game. In *Toss the Chips,* students drop a set of two-color counters and record the number of red and the number of yellow. Math Workshop focuses on decomposing numbers in different ways, and the session ends with a round of *Quick Images* using students' tile arrangements.	39	27, 28	• **Algebra Connections in This Unit**, p. 18

Classroom Routines See page 20 for an overview.

Calendar
- Monthly calendar

Today's Question
- *Today's Question* charts for sessions 4.2, 4.4, and 4.6. See instructions on pages 134, 143, and 153.

Patterns on the Pocket Chart
- Pocket Chart(s) or Sentence Pocket Chart

- Question Mark Cards (from Investigation 1)
- Pattern Blocks (6 of each color)
- Arrow Cards (from Investigation 1)
- Prepared cups or baggies of pattern blocks (1 per pair)

Attendance
- No materials needed

Materials to Gather	Materials to Prepare
• **Square color tiles** (1 bin per group) • **Glue sticks** • **Crayons, markers, or colored pencils** (that match the colors of the square tiles) • **Envelopes or folders** (for storing student work or arranging tiles throughout this Investigation; 1 per student; optional)	• **M23, Inch Grid Paper** Make copies. (3 per student plus extras as needed) • **Paper squares** Use a paper cutter to cut 50–60 one-inch construction paper squares per student in colors to match tiles. You may copy Inch Grid Paper (M23) onto colored construction paper and cut apart the squares.
• **Square color tiles** (10 per student) • **Small paper cups** (1 per student; optional) • **Materials for Six Tiles in All** See Session 4.1. • **Materials for *Build It/Change It*** See Session 3.6. • **Materials for the Counting Jar routine** (as you have set it up)	• **Counting Jar** Place 9 green cubes and 1 yellow cube in the jar.
• **Square color tiles** • **Materials for Six Tiles in All** See Session 4.1. • **Materials for the Counting Jar** See Session 4.2. • **Materials for *Build It/Change It*** See Sesssion 3.6.	
• **Two color counters** • **Materials for Arrangements of 5-to-10 Tiles** See Session 4.3. • **Materials for the Counting Jar routine** (as you have set it up) • **Several student representations of arrangements of 5, 6, or 7 tiles** (from Session 4.3) • **Square tiles** (10 per student) • **Small paper cups** (1 per student; optional)	• **M24, *Toss the Chips*** Make copies. (as needed)

Ways to Make Numbers, *continued*

	Student Activity Book	Student Math Handbook Flip Chart	Professional Development: Read Ahead of Time	
SESSION 4.5 p. 148				
Quick Images in Pairs Students use their tile arrangements to play *Quick Images in Pairs*. Math Workshop focuses on decomposing numbers in different ways. The session ends with students acting out and solving several story problems.		27, 28, 31–34		
SESSION 4.6 p. 153				
Combinations of 6 Math Workshop focuses on decomposing numbers in different ways. Class discussion focuses on the combinations that come up when 6 two-color counters are tossed.		27, 28		
SESSION 4.7 p. 157				
Arrangements of 6 Students compare different arrangements of six and discuss what they notice. Math Workshop continues, and students begin choosing a favorite arrangement for each number from 5 to 10, to combine into their own book of ways to make numbers.	40	27, 28	• **Dialogue Box:** Different Ways to See a Shape, p. 185	

Materials to Gather	Materials to Prepare
• **Student arrangements of 5, 6, or 7 tiles** • **Square tiles** (10 per student) • **Small paper cups** (1 per student; optional) • **Materials for the** *Toss the Chips* See Session 4.4. • **Materials for Arrangements of 5-to-10 Tiles** See Session 4.3. • **Materials for the Counting Jar routine** (as you have set it up)	
• **Materials for** *Quick Images in Pairs* See Session 4.5. • **Materials for** *Toss the Chips* See Session 4.4. • **Materials for Arrangements of 5-to-10 Tiles** See Session 4.3. • **Materials for the Counting Jar routine** (as you have set it up) • **Two-color counters** (6)	• **Chart paper** Copy onto chart paper the *Toss the Chips* (M24) table
• **Envelope or folder of completed arrangements of tiles** (1 per student) • **Stapler** • **Materials for** *Quick Images in Pairs* See Session 4.5. • **Materials for** *Toss the Chips* See Session 4.4.	• **M25, My Favorite Arrangement** Make copies. (optional) • **Student arrangements of 6 tiles** Look for particular arrangements such as a 2-by-3 rectangle, and what students often call "the staircase," "the Z," and "the T." (See page 158). If your students have not made these arrangements, choose pairs of arrangements that could be described in the same way numerically (e.g., 2 arrangements that could be described as 2 and 2 and 2).

Ways to Make Numbers,
continued

	Student Activity Book	Student Math Handbook Flip Chart	Professional Development: Read Ahead of Time	
SESSION 4.8　　　　p. 162				
End-of-Unit Assessment and Arrangements of Numbers　While students continue to decompose numbers in different ways during Math Workshop, students who have not yet met the benchmarks for this unit meet individually with the teacher. Depending on which benchmarks they have and have not met, they use cubes to measure the length of a shoe outline, count a set of 15 objects, and/or play a few rounds of *One More, One Fewer* with the teacher.	41		• **Teacher Note:** Learning About Length: Lining Up Units, p. 169 • **Teacher Note:** Assessing *One More, One Fewer,* p. 176	
SESSION 4.9　　　　p. 165				
End-of-Unit Assessment and Arrangements of Seven　Students continue to decompose numbers in different ways during Math Workshop while students who have not yet met the benchmarks meet individually with the teacher. Class discussion focuses on different ways to make 7.		27, 28		

Materials to Gather	Materials to Prepare
• **One shoe outline** (from Investigation 1) • **Connecting cubes** • **Primary Number Cards** (one deck, with Wild Cards removed) • **15 counters** • **Plus or Minus 1 Cube** • **Materials for Choosing Favorite Arrangements** See Session 4.7. • **Materials for** *Quick Images in Pairs* See Session 4.5. • **Materials for** *Toss the Chips* See Session 4.4. • **Completed and blank copies of Assessment Checklist M3, M15, M22** ☑	• **M13, Ten-Frame** Make copies. (as needed) • **List of students** Make a list of students that specifies which tasks to do with each student.
• **Materials for End-of-Unit Assessment** See Session 4.8. • **Materials for Choosing Favorite Arrangements** See Session 4.7. • **Materials for** *Quick Images in Pairs* See Session 4.5. • **Materials for** *Toss the Chips* See Session 4.4.	

☑ Checklist Available

Six Tiles in All

Math Focus Points

◆ Developing and analyzing visual images for quantities up to 10

◆ Creating a set of a given size

◆ Recording an arrangement of a quantity

Vocabulary

arrangement

Today's Plan			Materials
ACTIVITY **❶ Introducing Six Tiles in All**	🕐 5–10 MIN	👥 CLASS	• M23* • Square color tiles; paper squares*; glue sticks; crayons, markers, or colored pencils
ACTIVITY **❷ Six Tiles in All**	🕐 15–25 MIN	👤 INDIVIDUALS	• *Student Activity Book,* p. 37 • M23* • Materials from Activity 1; Envelopes or folders (optional)
DISCUSSION **❸ Sharing Our Arrangements**	🕐 10 MIN	👥 CLASS	• Students' recorded arrangements of 6
SESSION FOLLOW-UP **❹ Practice**			• *Student Activity Book,* p. 38

*See *Materials to Prepare,* p. 123.

Classroom Routines

Calendar: What's Missing? Remove two dates on the monthly calendar. Challenge students to tell you which cards are missing and how they know.

ACTIVITY

1 Introducing Six Tiles in All

5–10 MIN   CLASS

Lay six square tiles before the class and ask several volunteers to count them, reinforcing the idea of double-checking as an important strategy when counting. ❶

When students agree that there are six tiles, explain today's activity.

Today you are going to make **arrangements** of six tiles. You are going to take 6 square tiles and arrange or organize them. Your arrangements need to follow a special rule—each tile needs to touch another tile in some way.

Use tiles to build several sample arrangements that show a variety of different ways that tiles can touch. Leave each arrangement intact, and use a new set of six tiles for each new arrangement.

The tiles can touch at the corners.

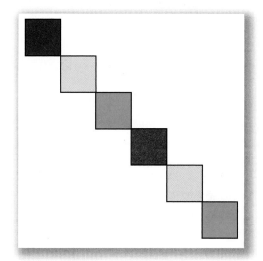

They can share part of a side.

They can share an entire side.

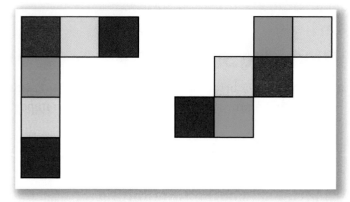

They can do some of each of these.

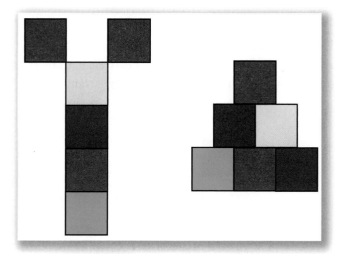

Then, make several arrangements that do *not* work and ask students to explain why they do not follow the rule.❷

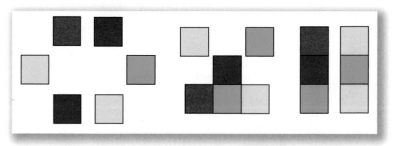

How would you arrange six tiles? Would someone show us his or her idea?

Here is [Tammy's] way. How many tiles do you think there are in [her] arrangement? Do you agree that there are six? How do you know? . . . Is there another way we could arrange these tiles to show six? . . . Does someone have a different idea? Would you show us? Does [Corey's] way follow the rule? Do all of the tiles touch in some way? . . .

When students understand the task and the fact that there is more than one possible arrangement, explain today's activity.

Your job today is to find different ways to arrange six tiles so that the tiles touch. You can make as many different arrangements as you like, but everyone needs to choose one way to record and share with the class.

Show students the Inch Grid Paper (M23), the coloring materials, and the paper squares and glue. Collect a few ideas about how students can use these materials to record, and then have students begin to work.

ACTIVITY

2 Six Tiles in All

15–25 MIN   INDIVIDUALS

Students work individually to find different ways to arrange six tiles so that all of the tiles touch in some way. They record one arrangement on *Student Activity Book* page 37 to share at the end of class.

Students find different ways to arrange six tiles.

ONGOING ASSESSMENT: Observing Students at Work ✔

Students find different ways to arrange six objects, reinforcing the idea that six is six, no matter how it is arranged. ❸

- **Do students' arrangements have six tiles?** Does each tile touch the tile next to it?

- **Do students find more than one solution?** On their own? At your request?

Professional Development

❸ **Teacher Note:** Counting Is More Than 1, 2, 3, p. 170 and Observing Kindergarteners as They Count, p. 171

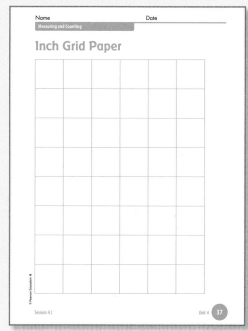

▲ **Student Activity Book, p. 37; Resource Masters, M23**

Teaching Note

❹ **Describing Arrangements** Some students may not have anything to say except "It's six." While it is important to encourage students to think of grouping the tiles mentally in some way, it may be sufficiently challenging for some just to count out and record six things. Others may have created an arrangement that does not in fact look like anything to them.

● **How do students name and describe their arrangements?** Do they focus on the overall image? The colors of the tiles? The number of tiles?

● **Can students accurately record an arrangement on grid paper?**

As you observe, note how students are counting, arranging, visualizing, and recording the tiles. Ask them to explain how they know they have six, and to think of ways to name or describe their arrangements.❹ Write students' responses on their recording sheets.

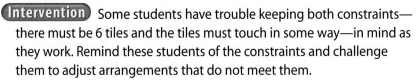

"It's like 2 overlapping squares."

"Each square has 4 tiles."

"I used 6 tiles."

DIFFERENTIATION: Supporting the Range of Learners

Intervention Some students have trouble keeping both constraints— there must be 6 tiles and the tiles must touch in some way—in mind as they work. Remind these students of the constraints and challenge them to adjust arrangements that do not meet them.

Some students acquire an extra tile or misplace one of the six they are working with. This may be a counting problem or the result of students working in close proximity. Encourage students to double-check their counting and to explain how they know that they have six tiles.

Some students need support in recording their work. Ask them to lay a sheet of grid paper next to their arrangement and to re-create the arrangement using construction paper squares. Then help them glue down one square at a time, or show them how to remove one square at a time and color it the appropriate color. Students who make arrangements in which tiles share parts of sides may find it easier to record on blank paper.

Dialogue Box: It Looks Like a Chair, p. 184

DISCUSSION

③ Sharing Our Arrangements

10 MIN   CLASS

Math Focus Points for Discussion

◆ Developing and analyzing visual images for quantities up to 10

Ask several students to hold up their representations and tell about them. There will be a variety of responses. Some students attend to the color or number of tiles; some consider their arrangement just "6" or "a design" or "a thing;" others see the overall image of the tiles as an object or letter.

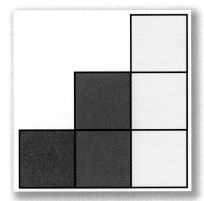

For the image above, strategies may focus on the overall visual image ("It looks like a staircase"), the colors ("It goes red, blue, blue, yellow, yellow, yellow"), the number of tiles in different parts of the arrangement ("It goes 1 then 2 then 3"), or some combination of these ("It's like steps—1, 2, 3").

After students have shared their arrangements, choose one design with an obvious shape (such as a T) and ask students how they would remember it if you asked them to build it. Accept different ways of viewing and remembering the arrangement.⑤ ⑥

SESSION FOLLOW-UP

④ Practice

 Practice: For reinforcement of this unit's content, have students complete *Student Activity Book* page 38.

Teaching Note

⑥ **Keeping Track of Student Work** Students will be arranging different numbers of square tiles and recording their work for the rest of this unit. They will eventually choose a favorite arrangement for each number from five through ten to make a book of "Ways to Make Numbers." Therefore, you may want to have students store their completed work in an envelope or folder.

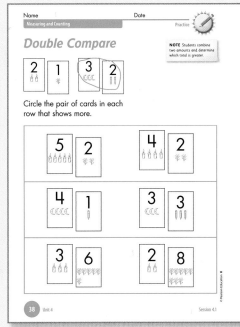

▲ **Student Activity Book, p. 38**

Quick Images: Square Tiles

Math Focus Points

◆ Developing and analyzing visual images for quantities up to 10

◆ Decomposing numbers in different ways

◆ Modeling the action of combining and separating situations

Today's Plan		Materials
ACTIVITY **①** *Quick Images: Square Tiles*	🕐 10–15 MIN 👥 CLASS	• Square color tiles of one color; small paper cups (optional)
MATH WORKSHOP **②** **Counting and Arranging** ㉔ **Six Tiles in All** ㉕ **Counting Jar** ㉖ *Build It/Change It*	🕐 15–20 MIN	㉔ • Materials from Session 4.1, p. 128 ㉕ • Counting Jar* • Materials for the Counting Jar (as you have set it up) ㉖ • Materials from Session 3.6, p. 113
ACTIVITY **③** **Acting Out Story Problems**	🕐 5–10 MIN 👥 CLASS	
SESSION FOLLOW-UP **④** **Practice**		• *Student Math Handbook Flip Chart*, pp. 20, 27, 28, 31–34

*See *Materials to Prepare,* p. 123.

Classroom Routines

Today's Question: Do You Have an Older Sister? On chart paper, create a two-column table titled "Do you have an older sister?" with the headings "Yes" written at the top of one column and "No" at the top of the other column. Students respond by writing their names below the appropriate heading. Count the responses as a class and discuss what the results of the survey tell you.

ACTIVITY

1 *Quick Images: Square Tiles*

10–15 MIN CLASS

Explain that today you will do *Quick Images* with square tiles. Give each student a set of about ten square tiles of one color, perhaps in a paper cup.❶❷ Then show students the following image.

What can you tell me about this arrangement?

Students might say:

 "It's like an S."

 "There are two squares that stick out on each side."

 "There are two rows of three."

All observations are important as students look carefully at the arrangement and begin making sense of it.

Look carefully at the arrangement because I'm going to cover it up. Try to find a way to remember what it looks like so that when it's covered, you'll be able to see it in your mind.

Hide the arrangement from view and challenge students to use the square tiles in their paper cup to build a copy of it.❸ Keep in mind that students may vary widely in how comfortable they are with seeing, remembering, and analyzing visual images.

Show the arrangement again, then cover it and give students another minute or two to work. Then, uncover the arrangement and let those students who need to do so adjust their work.

Teaching Notes

❶ **Preparing to do *Quick Images*** This session is written as if there is a space where students can gather, view an arrangement of actual tiles, and use tiles to recreate that arrangement. If it is not possible for them gather in a way to see an arrangement of tiles, draw the images on chart paper or use transparent square tiles on the overhead projector, to display the images.

❷ **Using One Color for *Quick Images*** Although students have been using different colors of tiles to make arrangements, use only one color to introduce *Quick Images* to the class. This will encourage students to focus on the overall shape of the image and enable them to see it in different ways.

❸ **"But my tiles are red!"** While all students have square tiles of one color, some may be distracted by the fact that they are a color other than blue. Encourage students to use their tiles to make an image with the same shape and the same number of tiles as your image. Some students may prefer to use blue paper squares to recreate your image.

That was challenging! When I covered the picture, how did you remember what it looked like? What helped you build a copy of my arrangement?

Students vary widely in how comfortable they are with describing what they remember. Some can describe and analyze a mental image they have formed, but others find this difficult. Focus the discussion on how they know how many squares there are, rather than just giving the total number of squares.

Repeat this activity once or twice, as time permits, using other arrangements of six tiles.

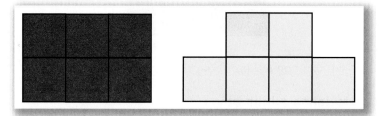

Follow the same process each time.

- Briefly show the arrangement.
- Students use square tiles to make a copy.
- Show the arrangement again.
- Students revise their work.
- Show the arrangement. Students describe the arrangement and discuss how they remembered what it looked like.

MATH WORKSHOP

2 Counting and Arranging

15–20 MIN

Explain that the following three activities, one of which is a new Counting Jar, are available during Math Workshop. Remind students what each activity entails, what materials are required, and where they are located.

2A Six Tiles in All

INDIVIDUALS

For complete details on this activity, see Session 4.1, page 129.

2B Counting Jar

INDIVIDUALS

Students count the objects in the Counting Jar—nine green cubes and one yellow cube. Then, they make a set of the same size and find a way to record what they found out.

Also, note whether students use the idea of one more when they count the cubes.

See Session 1.2, page 36, for what to observe.

Professional Development

 Teacher Note: Creating Your Own Story Problems, p. 172 and Story Problems in Kindergarten, p. 174

2C Build It/Change It

PAIRS

For complete details on this activity, see Session 3.6, page 114.

ACTIVITY

3 Acting Out Story Problems

5–10 MIN CLASS

As you did in Session 3.2, tell a story that involves combining or separating. Do not tell students which action the story involves. Ask several students to tell the story in their own words, and then ask volunteers to act it out. Finally, pose a problem about the story and gather solution strategies.

Tell several stories, presenting some in which students themselves can represent each quantity (e.g., stories about people or animals), and others where students can use props to show the quantities (e.g., stories about pennies, blocks, or other classroom objects).

As students become more comfortable with this process, vary the activity as follows:

Use stories about two children so that students can act out the stories in pairs. When everyone has had a chance to act out the story with a partner, pose a question about the story and gather solution strategies.

Pose the entire story problem to the class at once—the story and the question at the end. Give students time to work with a partner to act out and solve the problem in any way that makes sense to them. Some pairs might want to try modeling the story with counters or pictures instead of acting it out. When everyone has solved the problem, invite students to explain their solution strategies to the class.

SESSION FOLLOW-UP

4 Practice

Student Math Handbook Flip Chart: Use the *Student Math Handbook Flip Chart* pages 20, 27, 28, 31–34 to reinforce concepts from today's session. See pages 186–190 in the back of this unit.

Arrangements of 5 to 10 Tiles

Math Focus Points

◆ Creating a set of a given size

◆ Developing and analyzing visual images for quantities up to 10

◆ Decomposing numbers in different ways

◆ Recording an arrangement of a quantity

Today's Plan		Materials
1 ACTIVITY **Introducing Arrangements of 5 to 10 Tiles**	5–10 MIN CLASS	• Square color tiles
2 MATH WORKSHOP **More Counting and Arranging** 2A **Arrangements of 5 to 10 Tiles** 2B **Counting Jar** 2C *Build It/Change It*	20–30 MIN	2A • Materials from Session 4.1, p. 128 2B • Materials from Session 4.2, p. 134 2C • Materials from Session 3.6, p. 113
3 DISCUSSION **Checking In**	5 MIN CLASS	
4 SESSION FOLLOW-UP **Practice**		• *Student Math Handbook Flip Chart*, pp. 20, 27

Classroom Routines

Patterns on the Pocket Chart: What Comes Next? Arrange an ABCD repeating pattern on the pocket chart using ten pattern blocks (green triangle, blue rhombus, yellow hexagon, orange square). Follow the basic *Patterns* activity. Students hold up the block that they think is under each Question Mark Card.

5–10 MIN   CLASS

ACTIVITY

1 Introducing Arrangements of 5 to 10 Tiles

For the last few days, you have been making arrangements of six tiles in which all of the tiles touch in some way. Today's activity is similar to Six Tiles in All.

Now you can make arrangements for any of the numbers from 5 through 10. You can make arrangements with five tiles, arrangements with six tiles, or arrangements with seven, eight, nine, or ten tiles. Let's try the number 8 as an example.

Show students a set of eight tiles. Ask several volunteers to count them, reinforcing the idea that double-checking is an important counting strategy. When the class agrees that there are eight, ask students to think for a moment about how they may arrange the tiles. Ask a volunteer to share an idea with the class.

Here is [Lionel's] way. How many tiles do you think there are in his arrangement? Do you agree that there are eight? How do you know? Does [Lionel's] way follow the rule? Do all of the tiles touch in some way? Is there another way we could arrange these tiles to show eight? Does someone have a different idea?

Ask another volunteer to use another set of eight tiles to model another idea. Make sure that students understand the task and the fact that there is more than one possible arrangement.

Your job over the next few days is to find different ways to arrange different numbers of tiles. Just as you did when you worked with six, you can make as many arrangements as you like, but you need to record *at least two* arrangements for each number from five to ten. Then, we'll make your favorite arrangements into a book—there will be a five page, a six page, a seven page, an eight page, a nine page, and a ten page.

MATH WORKSHOP

2 More Counting and Arranging

20–30 MIN

Explain that the following three activities are available during Math Workshop and that today is the last day *Build It/Change It* will be available. Remind students what each activity entails, what materials are required, and where they are located.

2A Arrangements of 5 to 10 Tiles

INDIVIDUALS

Students work individually to find different ways to arrange sets of square color tiles. They record at least two arrangements for each number from 5 to 10.

Students find different ways to arrange a set of 5-to-10 tiles.

ONGOING ASSESSMENT: Observing Students at Work

Students arrange a set of objects in different ways, reinforcing the idea that a quantity is a quantity, no matter how it is arranged.

- **Do students' arrangements use the correct number of tiles?** Do they follow the rule that all tiles must touch in some way?

- **How do students name and describe their arrangements?** Do they focus on the overall image? The colors of the tiles? The number of tiles?

- **Can students accurately record an arrangement on grid paper?**

As you observe, note how students are counting, arranging, visualizing, and recording the tiles. Ask them to tell you how many tiles they have, to explain how they know, and to think of ways to name or describe their arrangements. Write students' responses on their recording sheets.

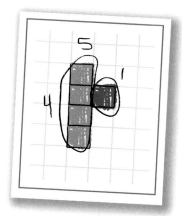

Sample Student Work

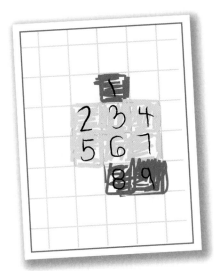

Sample Student Work

DIFFERENTIATION: Supporting the Range of Learners

(**Intervention**) Some students have trouble keeping both constraints in mind as they work. Remind them to double-check their count and that their tiles must touch, as needed. Challenge students to figure out how to make an arrangement that does not fit the rule into one that does.

2B Counting Jar

INDIVIDUALS

For complete details about this activity, see Session 4.2, page 136.

2C Build It/Change It

PAIRS

For complete details about this activity, see Session 3.6, page 114.

DISCUSSION

Checking In

🕐 **5 MIN** 👥 **CLASS**

Take this opportunity to discuss any difficulties that you noticed while observing students at work. The topic may be mathematical in nature, such as a strategy you would like all students to consider (e.g., using numbers to describe an arrangement) or a common error or misconception you would like students to discuss (e.g., making arrangements that fit the rules).

The issue could be logistical (such as sharing strategies for gluing down squares) or management-related (for example, working independently, sharing and cleaning up materials).

Other alternatives include checking in with students about which activities they have been choosing (e.g., "Thumbs up if you worked on Arrangements of 5 to 10 Tiles. Thumbs up if you worked on Counting Jar."), asking everyone to hold up a piece of work, or allowing students to raise a question or make a comment about today's math class.

SESSION FOLLOW-UP

Practice

Student Math Handbook Flip Chart: Use the *Student Math Handbook Flip Chart* pages 20, 27 to reinforce concepts from today's session. See pages 186–190 in the back of this unit.

Toss the Chips

Math Focus Points

◆ Decomposing numbers in different ways

◆ Using numbers to record how many

◆ Developing and analyzing visual images for quantities up to 10

Today's Plan		Materials
1 ACTIVITY **Introducing *Toss the Chips***	5–10 MIN CLASS	• *Student Activity Book*, p. 39 or M24* • Two color counters

2 MATH WORKSHOP
Counting, Arranging, and Recording
2A *Toss the Chips*
2B Arrangements of 5 to 10 Tiles
2C Counting Jar
	15–25 MIN	**2A** • *Student Activity Book*, p. 39
		   • M24*
		   • Two color counters
		2B • Materials from Session 4.3, p. 138
		2C • Materials from Session 4.2, p. 134

3 ACTIVITY ***Quick Images***	10 MIN CLASS	• Student representations of arrangements of 5, 6, or 7 tiles • Square tiles; small paper cups (optional)
4 SESSION FOLLOW-UP **Practice**		• *Student Math Handbook Flip Chart*, pp. 27, 28

*See *Materials to Prepare*, p. 123.

Classroom Routines

Today's Question: Would You Rather be a Monkey or an Elephant? On chart paper, create a two-column table titled "Would you rather be a monkey or an elephant?" with the label "Monkey" at the bottom of one column and "Elephant" at the bottom of the other. Students respond by writing their names above the appropriate label. Count the responses as a class and discuss what the results of the survey tell you.

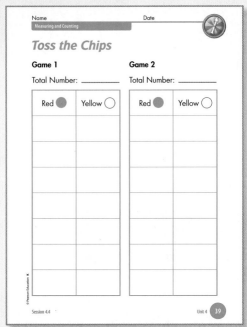

▲ **Student Activity Book, p. 39;**
Resource Masters, M24

5–10 MIN   CLASS

ACTIVITY

① Introducing *Toss the Chips*

Toss the Chips is an activity that involves separating a quantity into two parts. Select four 2-color counters and ask a student sitting close to you to verify how many counters you have in your hand.

I have four counters in my hand. These counters are red on one side, and yellow on the other. I'm going to drop the counters and see how many land with the red side facing up and how many land with the yellow side facing up.

Toss the counters and ask students what happened.

How many counters landed with the red side facing up?

How many counters landed with the yellow side facing up?

How many counters are there in all?

Show students how to record this information on *Student Activity Book* page 39 or on *Toss the Chips* (M24). Write "4" on the line next to "Total Number," and record the number of red and yellow in the appropriate boxes in the second row.

Toss the Chips

Game 1		Game 2	
Total Number: **4**		Total Number: _____	
Red ⬤	Yellow ◯	Red ⬤	Yellow ◯
1	**3**		

Repeat the activity until you think students understand the steps. Be sure to model what happens if all of the counters land with the red or yellow side facing up to generate some ideas about how to record with zero.

MATH WORKSHOP

② Counting, Arranging, and Recording

15–25 MIN

Explain that the following three activities are available during Math Workshop. Remind students what each activity entails, what materials are required, and where they are located.

- -

②A Toss the Chips

INDIVIDUALS

Students play *Toss the Chips*. They can play individually or in pairs, but all students need to record each toss on *Student Activity Book* page 39 or *Toss the Chips* (M24). Suggest that students begin playing with five chips, or counters.

ONGOING ASSESSMENT: Observing Students at Work

Students explore combinations of a number.

- **How do students figure out the number of red and yellow?** Can they just see how many of each there are? Do they count? Use one amount to find the other? (for example, "I tossed 5 and 4 are red, so 1 is yellow, because 4 and 1 makes 5.")

- **Do students recognize combinations that repeat?**

- **Do students understand that the total number of counters is equivalent to the number of red counters and the number of yellow counters?**

- **Can students use numbers to record?** Can they write the numbers accurately? Do they use zero appropriately?

As you observe, ask students about their work. For example, choose a completed row and ask how many counters they tossed. Then, ask them to show you what that round looked like with 2-color counters.

- -

DIFFERENTIATION: Supporting the Range of Learners

Extension Students who complete one game (or *Student Activity Book* page 39) can play again with a different number of counters.

- -

②B Arrangements of 5 to 10 Tiles

INDIVIDUALS

For complete details about this activity, see Session 4.3, page 139.

During this time, find several examples of tile arrangements to use as images during the *Quick Images* activity at the end of this session. Choose arrangements that use 5, 6, or 7 tiles, that offer multiple ways to visualize and remember them, and that are recorded clearly. Also, choose arrangements that use only 1 or 2 colors, or where the use of color is helpful in remembering the image. Ask students whether you can use them for *Quick Images* and return them later.

2C Counting Jar

INDIVIDUALS

For complete details about this activity, see Session 4.2, page 136.

ACTIVITY

10 MIN CLASS

3 Quick Images

Show students the work you chose during Math Workshop. Give each student ten square tiles, perhaps in a paper cup.

We are going to do Quick Images with square tiles again today. But this time I am not going to use tiles. I am going to show you an arrangement of tiles that [Russell] made during Math Workshop.

Hold the piece of student work up for about five seconds.

*Remember, do not start building until I hide the picture. Spend this time looking carefully at the arrangement and thinking about how you will remember it after it is hidden.*❶

Then place the piece of student work facedown and challenge students to use their square tiles to recreate it.

I am going to show [Russell's] arrangement one more time. Are you ready?

Show the image for a few more seconds and then place it facedown until students are finished.

Here is [Russell's] arrangement. Look at your tiles. How did you do? What helped you remember what [Russell's] arrangement looked like?

Some students describe the overall shape or the shape of the parts while others talk about the total number of squares or the number of squares in each part.

Do the same for several pieces of student work as time permits. Follow the same process each time.

- Briefly show the arrangement.

- Students use square tiles to make a copy.

- Show the arrangement again.

- Students revise their work.

- Show the arrangement. Students describe the arrangement and discuss how they remembered what it looked like.

SESSION FOLLOW-UP

Practice

Student Math Handbook Flip Chart: Use the *Student Math Handbook Flip Chart* pages 27, 28 to reinforce concepts from today's session. See pages 186–190 in the back of this unit.

Quick Images in Pairs

Math Focus Points

◆ Developing and analyzing visual images for quantities up to 10

◆ Decomposing numbers in different ways

◆ Modeling the action of combining and separating situations

Today's Plan		Materials
① ACTIVITY **Introducing *Quick Images in Pairs***	5–10 MIN CLASS	• Student representations of arrangements of 5, 6, or 7 tiles; square tiles; small paper cups (optional)
② MATH WORKSHOP **More Counting, Arranging, and Recording** **2A** *Quick Images in Pairs* **2B** *Toss the Chips* **2C** Arrangements of 5 to 10 Tiles **2D** Counting Jar	15–25 MIN	**2A** • Students' representations of arrangements for 5, 6, or 7 tiles; square tiles **2B** • Materials from Session 4.4, p. 143 **2C** • Materials from Session 4.3, p. 138 **2D** • Materials from Session 4.2, p. 134
③ ACTIVITY **Acting Out Story Problems**	10 MIN CLASS	
④ SESSION FOLLOW-UP **Practice**		• *Student Math Handbook Flip Chart*, pp. 27, 28, 31–34

Classroom Routines

Calendar: How Many Days . . . ? Students use the calendar to determine how many days until a class event or holiday that will happen this month. Discuss students' strategies for determining the number of days.

ACTIVITY

① Introducing *Quick Images in Pairs*

5–10 MIN · CLASS

As you did at the end of Session 4.4, present a piece of student work that shows an arrangement of 5, 6, or 7 tiles as a *Quick Images*.

Explain that during Math Workshop students can play *Quick Images in Pairs*. Ask two volunteers to model how this will work for the class. Give each a recorded tile arrangement, and ask them to sit *next to* each other, each with a cup of square tiles.

[Mia] is going to show her image for five seconds. [Brad] needs to get ready to watch very carefully.

Discuss ways to count and keep track of five seconds, perhaps using the "one one thousand, two one thousand" strategy, and then ask your volunteer to show the tile arrangement for five seconds.

I noticed that the whole time [Mia] was showing the picture, [Brad] was looking closely at the tile arrangement. Now that [Mia] put the picture down, [Brad] uses [his] tiles to try to build the tile arrangement [he] saw in the picture.❶

Ask the student to use the tiles and help from his classmates to make a first attempt at duplicating the tile arrangement.

Now, just like we do in class, [Mia] shows the picture one more time. After looking a second time, [Brad] makes any changes or additions to his tiles.

Finally, you work together to compare the tiles with the picture, to check that they are the same.

Teaching Note

❶ **"Do I have to use the same colors?"** This activity asks students to create an arrangement with the same overall shape and the same number of tiles; it does not need to use the same colors. However, some 5- and 6-year-olds have trouble *not* paying attention to the color of each tile. Encourage these students to try to focus on the overall shape and quantity, but know that they may need more than 2 looks at an image in order to remember and recreate it.

Lay the picture next to the tile arrangement, and ask students to compare the two.

Are they the same? How do you know?

Explain that pairs should work together to make the tile arrangement look exactly like the image, and then switch roles.

Now it is [Brad's] turn to hold up a picture and [Mia's] turn to use [her] tiles to try to build a copy.

MATH WORKSHOP

15–25 MIN

2 More Counting, Arranging, and Recording

Explain that the following four activities are available during Math Workshop. Remind students what each activity entails, what materials are required, and where they are located.

 Quick Images in Pairs

PAIRS

Player 1 shows a tile arrangement for five seconds, and then Player 2 tries to build it with square tiles. After a second look and some work time, players work together to compare the picture and the tile arrangement. Then players change roles.

After one student tries to build the other student's arrangement with tiles, they compare their arrangements.

ONGOING ASSESSMENT: Observing Students at Work

Students develop strategies for analyzing and remembering visual images of quantities.

- **How do students make sense of and analyze the visual images of quantities?** Do they focus on the overall shape? The shape of different parts? How different parts are related to one another? The colors of the tiles? The number of tiles?

- **Can students build an accurate copy of a pictured tile arrangement?**

DIFFERENTIATION: Supporting the Range of Learners

Intervention For some students, using tiles to build a copy of a pictured arrangement is challenging enough with the picture in view the entire time.

If some students' recorded tile arrangements are difficult to interpret, encourage them to build an arrangement with tiles and cover it with a sheet of paper. Then, Player 1 removes the piece of paper and Player 2 builds a copy of the arrangement.

2B *Toss the Chips*

INDIVIDUALS

For complete details about this activity, see Session 4.4, page 144.

2C Arrangements of 5 to 10 Tiles

INDIVIDUALS

For complete details about this activity, see Session 4.3, page 139.

2D Counting Jar

INDIVIDUALS

For complete details about this activity, see Session 4.2, page 136.

ACTIVITY

3 Acting out Story Problems

10 MIN   CLASS

As you did in Session 3.2, tell a story that involves combining or separating. Do not tell students which action the story involves. Ask several students to tell the story in their own words, and then ask volunteers to act it out. Finally, pose a problem about the story and gather solution strategies.

Tell several stories, presenting some where students themselves can represent each quantity (e.g., stories about people or animals), and others in which students can use props to show the quantities (e.g., stories about pennies, blocks, or other classroom objects).

As students become more comfortable with this process, vary the activity as follows:

Use stories about two children so that students can act out the stories in pairs. When everyone has had a chance to act out the story with a partner, pose a question about the story and gather solution strategies.

Pose the entire story problem to the class at once—the story and the question at the end. Give students time to work with a partner to act out and solve the problem in any way that makes sense to them. Some pairs may want to try modeling the story with counters or pictures instead of acting it out. When everyone has solved the problem, invite students to explain their solution strategies to the class.

SESSION FOLLOW-UP

4 Practice

Student Math Handbook Flip Chart: Use the *Student Math Handbook Flip Chart* pages 27, 28, 31–34 to reinforce concepts from today's session. See pages 186–190 in the back of this unit.

Combinations of Six

Math Focus Points

- Developing and analyzing visual images for quantities up to 10
- Decomposing numbers in different ways
- Exploring combinations of a number (e.g., 6 is 3 and 3 and also 5 and 1)

Today's Plan		Materials
1 MATH WORKSHOP **More Counting, Arranging, and Recording** **1A** *Quick Images in Pairs* **1B** *Toss the Chips* **1C** Arrangements of 5 to 10 Tiles **1D** Counting Jar	20–35 MIN	**1A** • Materials from Session 4.5, p. 148 **1B** • Materials from Session 4.4, p. 143 **1C** • Materials from Session 4.3, p. 138 **1D** • Materials from Session 4.2, p. 134
2 DISCUSSION **Tossing Six Chips**	10 MIN CLASS	• Large chart paper version and students' completed copies of *Student Activity Book*, p. 39*; two-color counters
3 SESSION FOLLOW-UP **Practice**		• *Student Math Handbook Flip Chart*, pp. 27, 28

*See *Materials to Prepare,* p. 125.

Classroom Routines

Today's Question: Are You Wearing Any Zippers Today? On chart paper, create a vertical two-column table titled "Are you wearing any zippers today?" with the label "Yes" at the top of one column and "No" written at the top of the other column. Students respond by writing their names below the appropriate heading. Count the responses as a class and discuss what the results of the survey tell you.

MATH WORKSHOP

① More Counting, Arranging, and Recording

20–35 MIN

Explain that the following four activities are available during Math Workshop. Remind students what each activity entails, what materials are required, and where they are located.

In preparation for the discussion at the end of this session, ask all students to play one round of *Toss the Chips* today, using six counters.

1A *Quick Images in Pairs*

PAIRS

For complete details about this activity, see Session 4.5, page 149.

DIFFERENTIATION: Supporting the Range of Learners

Extension Some students may like the challenge of doing *Quick Images* with tile arrangements for 8, 9, and 10. Encourage these students to show the picture three times instead of two, as needed.

1B Toss the Chips

INDIVIDUALS

For complete details about this activity, see Session 4.4, page 144.

1C Arrangements of 5 to 10 Tiles

INDIVIDUALS

For complete details about this activity, see Session 4.3, page 139.

1D Counting Jar

INDIVIDUALS

For complete details about this activity, see Session 4.2, page 136.

DISCUSSION

② Tossing Six Chips

Math Focus Points for Discussion

◆ Exploring combinations of a number (e.g., 6 is 3 and 3 and also 5 and 1)

End this session by collecting some of the combinations of six that came up when students tossed six two-color counters. Post the chart *"Toss the Chips"*. Ask students to bring their completed copy of this sheet from when they played with six chips.

As I was watching you toss the chips, I noticed that there are many different ways the counters can land. What are some of the ways you found?

Students might say:

"I got three red and three yellow."

Does that equal six? Did [Carmen] toss six counters? How do you know?

Students might say:

"Count all of the chips. There are six."

"I counted on my fingers. First I counted three, and then I counted another three. That equals six."

"I just know that three plus three equals six."

Model each strategy that students suggest.

Everyone look at your paper. Raise your hand if you got three red and three yellow, too. ❶

Algebra Note

❷ **Opposites** Some students notice particular pairs of combinations (e.g., 2 red and 4 yellow and 4 red and 2 yellow) and name them "opposites". Ask these students what they mean, and challenge them to find other opposites for the number 6. See **Algebra Connections in This Unit,** p. 18.

Record each combination. As you do, ask a volunteer to model the suggestion with counters, to help students develop visual images of combinations of 6.

Many people got 3 red and 3 yellow. I am going to write that on our chart. [Yoshio], could you show us what that would look like with the counters?

Then, ask students to check their papers for a different combination.

[Carmen] got 3 red and 3 yellow. Who got something different?

Encourage students to check their papers for ways that are not already recorded, but know that kindergarteners are likely to suggest combinations that have already been shared.❷

Continue until there are no new combinations to share. You may end with an open-ended question.

Do you think that we have all the ways to make 6 with red and yellow counters? Do you think there are other ways? You might think about this question the next time you play Toss the Chips.

Save the table you made of the combinations for six chips for tomorrow's discussion.

SESSION FOLLOW-UP
Practice

Student Math Handbook Flip Chart: Use the *Student Math Handbook Flip Chart* pages 27, 28 to reinforce concepts from today's session. See pages 186–190 in the back of this unit.

Arrangements of 6

Math Focus Points

◆ Developing and analyzing visual images for quantities up to 10

◆ Decomposing numbers in different ways

◆ Recording an arrangement of a quantity

Today's Plan		Materials
① DISCUSSION **Different Arrangements of 6**	10 MIN CLASS	• Students' arrangements of 6 tiles*
② ACTIVITY **Introducing Choosing Favorite Arrangements**	5 MIN CLASS	• *Student Activity Book*, p. 40 • M25 (optional)* • Envelope or folder of completed arrangements of tiles
③ MATH WORKSHOP **Arrangements and Combinations** **3A** *Choosing Favorite Arrangements* **3B** *Quick Images in Pairs* **3C** *Toss the Chips*	15–25 MIN	**3A** • *Student Activity Book*, p. 40 • Envelope or folder of completed arrangements of tiles; stapler **3B** • Materials from Session 4.5, p. 148 **3C** • Materials from Session 4.4, p. 143
④ DISCUSSION **Checking In**	5 MIN CLASS	
⑤ SESSION FOLLOW-UP **Practice**		• *Student Math Handbook Flip Chart,* pp. 27, 28

*See *Materials to Prepare,* p. 125.

Classroom Routines

Patterns on the Pocket Chart: What Comes Next? Arrange an ABCD repeating pattern on the pocket chart using 10 pattern blocks (up, down, left, right). Follow the basic *Patterns* activity. Students point in the direction that they think is under each Question Mark Card.

DISCUSSION

Different Arrangements of 6

⏱ 10 MIN 👥 CLASS

Math Focus Points for Discussion

◆ Decomposing numbers in different ways

Hold up or hang up the two arrangements you have chosen (the one that looks like a staircase and the 2-by-3 rectangle or the alternate arrangements you chose). Ask students to look carefully at these two arrangements.

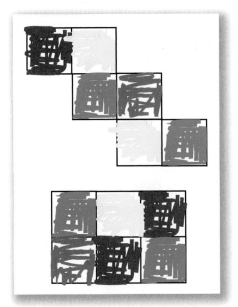

How are these arrangements different? How are they similar?

Students might say:

"They make different designs, but they both have 6 tiles."

"I see groups. There's 2 and 2 and 2."

If students do not bring up how the arrangements are broken up numerically, bring it up yourself.

Some people may say that the tiles in [Lisa's] arrangement are in groups: 2 here and 2 here and 2 here or 3 here and 3 here. How would you describe [Timothy's] arrangement with numbers? Do you think it is the same as [Lisa's] or different?

Some students will see the tiles in these arrangements broken up into 2 and 2 and 2 and others will see them broken up into 3 and 3.

One way we can arrange 6 tiles is 2 and 2 and 2 and another way we can arrange 6 tiles is 3 and 3.

Record students' ways of seeing the arrangements.❶

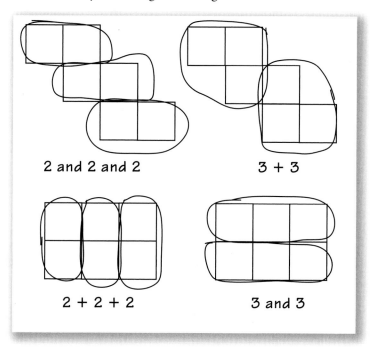

2 and 2 and 2   3 + 3

2 + 2 + 2   3 and 3

Look together at one or two more arrangements of 6 tiles and ask students to describe them with numbers.

How would you describe this arrangement with numbers? . . . Would anyone describe it in a different way?

As you did earlier, sketch each arrangement and record the ways students see it.❷ ❸

Teaching Notes

❶ **Addition Vocabulary and Notation** Some students use the word "plus " in their descriptions (2 plus 2 plus 2). Discuss this as it comes up, but know that students will be formally introduced to addition vocabulary and notation in *Counting and Measuring.*

❷ **Combinations of 6** Some students may notice that they are describing their tile arrangements with the same numbers that came up in the discussion about *Toss the Chips* at the end of Session 4.6. Discuss this if it arises, comparing today's chart paper with the one from yesterday.

Professional Development

❸ **Dialogue Box:** Different Ways to See a Shape, p. 185

Teaching Notes

❹ A Class Book You may want to compile a class book of *Our Favorite Arrangements,* in addition to the ones students will make. If this is the case, ask students to donate (or create duplicate copies of) arrangements for the class book. Use My Favorite Arrangement (M25) as a cover.

❺ Assembling a Portfolio As students sort through their recorded tile arrangements, choose one or more examples to include in their portfolio. Know that students will revisit this activity, with a focus on using numbers and notation to describe arrangements, in *How Many Do You Have?* (unit 6).

▲ **Student Activity Book, p. 40**

ACTIVITY
5 MIN   CLASS

② Introducing Choosing Favorite Arrangements

Explain that during Math Workshop today and tomorrow, students will be choosing their favorite arrangements of tiles for each number from 5 to 10 to create their own book of My Favorite Arrangements. Show them *Student Activity Book* page 40, which they will use as a cover for their book, and explain how they will staple the pages together to make a book.❹

MATH WORKSHOP

15–25 MIN

③ Arrangements and Combinations

Explain that the following three activities are available during Math Workshop. Remind students what each activity entails, what materials are required, and where they are located.

③A Choosing Favorite Arrangements

INDIVIDUALS

Students choose their favorite arrangements for the numbers 5 to 10 and staple them into a book of My Favorite Arrangements.

ONGOING ASSESSMENT: Observing Students at Work

Students collect arrangements of different numbers of square tiles.

- **How do students choose their favorite arrangements?** How do they name and describe them? By overall shape? By the shape and relationship between different parts? By the colors of the tiles? By the number of tiles in the arrangement or in different parts?

- **Do students put their pages in the correct numerical order?**

  As you help students staple their books, ask them how they would name or describe some of their arrangements and help them write those descriptions on the corresponding pages.❺

DIFFERENTIATION: Supporting the Range of Learners

 **Intervention** Talk with students to help ensure that they include an example of every number from 5 through 10.

3B *Quick Images in Pairs*

 INDIVIDUALS

For complete details about this activity, see Session 4.5, page 149.

3C *Toss the Chips*

For complete details about this activity, see Session 4.4, page 144.

DISCUSSION

Checking In

5 MIN | **CLASS**

Take this opportunity to discuss any difficulties that you noticed while observing students at work. The topic might be mathematical in nature, such as a strategy you would like all students to consider (e.g., ways students have to remember a tile arrangement in *Quick Images in Pairs*) or a common error or misconception you would like students to discuss (e.g., putting My Favorite Arrangement pages in the wrong order, not choosing one for each number).

The difficulty may be logistical (e.g., keeping track of pages for My Favorite Arrangement book) or management related (e.g., working independently).

Other alternatives include checking in with students about which activities they have been choosing (e.g., "Who began working on their book of My Favorite Arrangement today? Has everyone had a chance to do *Quick Images in Pairs*?"), asking everyone to hold up a piece of work, or allowing students to raise a question or make a comment about today's math class.⑥

SESSION FOLLOW-UP

Practice

Student Math Handbook Flip Chart: Use the *Student Math Handbook Flip Chart* pages 27, 28 to reinforce concepts from today's session. See pages 186–190 in the back of this unit.

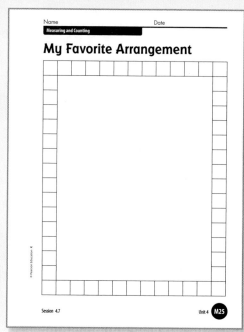

Name _____ Date _____

Measuring and Counting

My Favorite Arrangement

© Pearson Education K

Session 4.7   Unit 4 **M25**

▲ **Resource Masters, M25**

Teaching Note

⑥ **Preparing for the End-of-Unit Assessment**
Before Session 4.8, gather the assessment checklists you have filled in over the course of this unit: Assessment Checklist: Measuring Lengths (M3), Assessment Checklist: Counting (M15), and Assessment Checklist: *One More, One Fewer* (M22). For each benchmark, look over your notes, and sort students into three categories:

• Those who have clearly met the benchmark.

• Those who have not yet met the benchmark.

• Those about whom you have questions.

You will be meeting with students in the latter two categories over the course of Sessions 4.8 and 4.9. Make a list of students you need to meet with that specifies which tasks you need to do with each student.

End-of-Unit Assessment and Arrangements of Numbers

Math Focus Points

◆ Decomposing numbers in different ways

◆ Developing and analyzing visual images for quantities up to 10

Today's Plan	Materials

MATH WORKSHOP
 ① Arrangements and Assessment   ⏱ **25–40 MIN**
    ⓐ End-of-Unit Assessments
    ⓑ Choosing Favorite Arrangements
    ⓒ *Quick Images in Pairs*
    ⓓ *Toss the Chips*
	ⓐ • M13*; completed and blank copies of M3 ☑, M15 ☑, and M22 ☑
	 • One shoe outline; connecting cubes; Primary Number Cards; 15 counters; Plus or Minus 1 Cube; list of students*
	 ⓑ • Materials from Session 4.7, p. 157
	 ⓒ • Materials from Session 4.5, p. 148
	 ⓓ • Materials from Session 4.4, p. 143

DISCUSSION **② Checking In** ⏱ **5 MIN** 👪 **CLASS**	
SESSION FOLLOW-UP **③ Practice**	• *Student Activity Book*, p. 41

*See *Materials to Prepare,* p. 127.

Classroom Routines

Calendar: Mixed Up Calendar Choose two days-of-the-week cards and change their position on the calendar so that they are out of order. Challenge students to find the mistakes and help you fix them.

MATH WORKSHOP

Arrangements and Assessment

25–40 MIN   INDIVIDUALS

Explain that the following three activities are available during Math Workshop. Remind students what each activity entails, what materials are required, and where they are located.

- Choosing Favorite Arrangements (see Session 4.7)

- *Quick Images in Pairs* (see Session 4.5)

- *Toss the Chips* (see Session 4.4)

Explain that, while students are at work on these activities, you will be meeting individually with students. Review any policies you have about such a work time. For example, some teachers have an "ask three before me" rule, which requires that students ask three peers before coming to the teacher with a question.

While students are working on these activities, meet individually with those you need to assess.❶ ❷

Benchmark 1: Measure the length of an object by lining up multiple units.❸

Give students a shoe outline and a container of cubes. Ask them to show you how they would use the cubes to measure the length of the shoe. Note whether students do the following:

- Measure the length of the object

- Line up the first cube with the edge of the shoe outline

- Make a straight line of cubes from one end of the shoe to the other

Benchmark 2: Accurately count a set of up to 15 objects.❹

Give students a set of 15 loose cubes. Ask them to count them to find out how many there are. Note whether students:

- Know the names and the sequence of the numbers

- Count each object once and only once (which involves having a system for keeping track of what has been counted and what remains to be counted)

- Double-check

When they are finished counting, ask students how many cubes there are. Can students tell you the number, or do they recount the set to answer the question?

Teaching Note

❶ **Whom Should I Meet With?** In order to decide who to meet with individually, gather the three assessment checklists you have filled in over the course of this unit: Assessment Checklist: Measuring Lengths (M3), Assessment Checklist: Counting (M15), and Assessment Checklist: *One More, One Fewer* (M22). For each benchmark, look over your notes, and sort students into these three categories:

- Those who have clearly met the benchmark.

- Those who have not yet met the benchmark.

- Those you have questions about.

Do the assessment tasks with students in the latter two categories.

Differentiation

❷ **English Language Learners** English Language Learners may understand the math concepts in the End-of-Unit Assessment but may still have difficulty with instructions or questions in English. If this is the case, consider having a speaker of the student's native language—either an adult or a more English-proficient student—provide translation during the assessment.

Professional Development

❸ **Teacher Note** Learning About Length: Lining Up Units, p. 169

❹ **Teacher Notes** Counting is More Than 1, 2, 3, p. 170; Observing Kindergarteners As They Count, p. 171

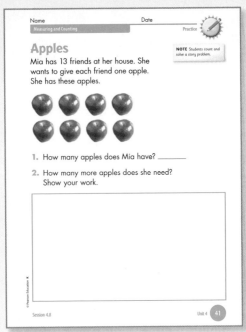

▲ **Student Activity Book, p. 41**

Professional Development

⑤ **Teacher Note** Assessing *One More, One Fewer,* p. 176

Benchmark 3: Figure out what is one more or one fewer than a number.⑤

Explain that you would like to play a few rounds of *One More, One Fewer*. Flip the top card and ask the student to place that many pennies on the Ten-Frame. Then roll the Plus or Minus 1 Cube, and ask the student to solve the problem. Play enough rounds so that students solve both one more and one fewer problems, and problems that involve a variety of starting numbers. Note whether students do the following:

• Accurately tell you what is one more or fewer than a given number

• Need to add or remove a penny

• Count from one or use some other strategy (count on or back, use the calendar or number line, and so on)

DISCUSSION

② **Checking In**

5 MIN   CLASS

Take this opportunity to check in with the class. Because you have been meeting individually with students, you may want to discuss any management problems (e.g., noise level, asking a friend before asking the teacher) that arose. You may also want to check in with students about which activities they worked on (e.g., "Thumbs up if you have finished your book of My Favorite Arrangement. Thumbs up if you're not quite done yet.") or allowing students to raise a question or make a comment about today's math class.

SESSION FOLLOW-UP

③ **Practice**

 Practice: For enrichment, have students complete *Student Activity Book* page 41.

End-of-Unit Assessment and Arrangements of 7

Math Focus Points

◆ Decomposing numbers in different ways

◆ Developing and analyzing visual images for quantities up to 10

Today's Plan		Materials
MATH WORKSHOP **① Arrangements and Assessment** **1A** Choosing Favorite Arrangements **1B** *Quick Images in Pairs* **1C** *Toss the Chips*	20–35 MIN	**1A** • Materials from Session 4.7, p. 157 **1B** • Materials from Session 4.5, p. 148 **1C** • Materials from Session 4.4, p. 143
DISCUSSION **② Arrangements of 7**	10 MIN CLASS	• My Favorite Arrangements book
SESSION FOLLOW-UP **③ Practice**		• *Student Math Handbook Flip Chart,* pp. 27, 28

Classroom Routines

Attendance: How Many Have Counted? Count around the circle as usual but pause several times during the count to ask students how many people have counted so far and how they know. Help students see why the number they say represents the number of students who have counted so far and that the last number represents the total number of students in class today.

Teaching Note

❶ Students Who Do Not Yet Meet the Benchmark
As you do the End-of-Unit Assessment interviews, you may come across a few students who do not yet meet one or more of the benchmarks for this unit. Watch closely as these students complete the assessment tasks to figure out, as specifically as you can, what it is these students are struggling with. For example, do they need more practice with the names of the numbers? The sequence? Do they need to figure out a system for organizing and keeping track of a count? Are they not sure that the last number they say represents the number of objects in the group? With such specific information, you can plan next steps—from meeting with them one-on-one to working with a small group to assigning particular activities during Math Workshop—that match students' needs. Also, know that students will get further practice with these concepts in the units that follow.

MATH WORKSHOP

① Assessment Workshop

20–35 MIN

Explain that the following three activities are available during Math Workshop. Remind students what each activity entails, what materials are required, and where they are located.

- Choosing Favorite Arrangements (see Session 4.7)

- *Quick Images in Pairs* (see Session 4.5)

- *Toss the Chips* (see Session 4.4)

Explain that, while students are at work on these activities, you will be meeting individually with students.

While students are working on these activities, meet individually with those you need to assess. (See Session 4.8.)❶

DISCUSSION

② Arrangements of 7

10 MIN   CLASS

Math Focus Points for Discussion

◆ Decomposing numbers in different ways

Ask students to open their book, My Favorite Arrangements to the 7 page and hold it up for others to see. After students have had a chance to look over their peers' work, choose one arrangement and discuss ways to use numbers to describe it.

Here is [Kyle's] arrangement of 7. What do you notice? How would you describe it?

Students might say:

"It looks like a person."

How many tiles are in each part of the person?

"I see 3 for the body, 2 for the arms, and 2 for the feet."

So one way to arrange 7 tiles is 3 and 2 and 2.

Sketch the tile arrangement and circle the groups that your volunteer saw.

[Lisa] thought of [Kyle's] arrangement as 3 and 2 and 2. Did anyone see [Kyle's] arrangement in a different way?

Students might say:

"I saw it as 3 and 4."

"And I saw it as 5 and 2."

After students have had a chance to share the different ways they see one arrangement, choose one of the ways and ask the following:

One way we saw [Kyle's] arrangement was as 3 and 2 and 2. Does anyone else have an arrangement that you think is 3 and 2 and 2?

Ask students who volunteer to show their arrangements and to point out the groups. If no one has a similar arrangement, move on to look at another and ask students to describe it with numbers.❷

Follow the same process with several more arrangements, as time permits.

SESSION FOLLOW-UP

③ Practice

Student Math Handbook Flip Chart: Use the *Student Math Handbook Flip Chart* pages 27, 28 to reinforce concepts from today's session. See pages 186–190 in the back of this unit.

Math Note

❷ **How Can These Be the Same?** Some students recognize that two arrangements can look very different but have similar groupings. For others, the fact that two arrangements look different makes it very hard for them to see similarities between them.

Professional Development

Measuring and Counting

In Part 6 of *Implementing Investigations in Kindergarten,* you will find a set of Teacher Notes that addresses topics and issues applicable to the curriculum as a whole rather than to specific curriculum units. They include the following:

Computational Fluency and Place Value

Computational Algorithms and Methods

Representations and Contexts for Mathematical Work

Foundations of Algebra in the Elementary Grades

Discussing Mathematical Ideas

Racial and Linguistic Diversity in the Classroom:
    What Does Equity Mean in Today's Math Classroom?

Learning About Length: Lining Up Units

In Kindergarten, students start working with ideas about what is *long, longer, short,* and *shorter.* Their ideas begin to develop as they compare lengths directly.

"My sister is taller than I am."

"My pencil is the shortest in the class."

Research on children's mathematical understanding shows that students typically do not develop a firm idea about length as a stable, measurable dimension until second grade, although there is quite a range of individual differences among students. Through many experiences with measuring and comparing, students develop their understanding of what length is and how it can be described.

Students in your class may vary quite a bit in how accurately and consistently they measure the lengths of things. Some do not carefully line up their sticks or cubes end to end when they use them to measure, instead either overlapping the units or leaving spaces between them. Others measure with a single object (such as a craft stick) by running it along a given length as they count "1, 2, 3, 4, . . ." without paying much attention to whether each successive placement begins where the previous one ended. These *mistakes* are probably not just carelessness or sloppiness; instead, these students are still figuring out what measuring is about.

Rather than simply tell students to carefully line up sticks along a length of tape, encourage discussion among students about the different ways they are measuring:

Some people said that this shelf was eight sticks long, some said nine, and some said eleven. Who would like to show how you measured this shelf? . . . Raul lined up eight sticks like this. Do you think that's all right? Could it be nine sticks? Could that work? Why or why not?

At times, you may show students some inaccurate ways of measuring to help them think through and articulate their own ideas. For example, spread out three sticks with big gaps along the edge of the shelf—one at the beginning of the shelf, one in the middle, and one lined up with the far end. Tell students that you measured this shelf and found that it was three sticks long. Ask them whether that is correct and, if not, what you should do to get a better measurement. As students discuss and compare ways of measuring, they will gradually grasp what length is and how to measure it accurately.

Students need to have many experiences with units that they can place repeatedly along a length and count (such as craft sticks, cubes, or their feet) so that they physically experience what length is, how it extends from one point to another, and how two lengths can be compared.

Because many students have seen people using rulers or yardsticks to measure objects, they may be interested in using such tools. You can make rulers available, but in the early grades, students usually see the numbers on a ruler simply as marks to read without understanding just how a ruler is used to quantify length. For example, some students align the end of an object with the 1, rather than with the end of the ruler. Others use the ruler backward, reporting a length of ten inches when it is actually two.

Students sometimes think that one measuring unit is equivalent to another; for example, they will find that an object is six cubes long and report the length as six inches. They may also think that when one object is longer than another, it must be one more unit long. For example, a 7-year-old who was four feet tall compared herself with a classmate. He was a few inches taller, so she said, "So he's five feet tall."

As students' understanding of measurement develops in Grades K–1, they begin to formulate ideas about the need for standard units of measure. The understanding they develop through many experiences of using nonstandard units will become the basis for understanding the use of standard measuring tools. The need for a standard measuring tool is among the topics students investigate in Grade 2 Measuring Length and Time.

Counting Is More Than 1, 2, 3

Counting is the basis for understanding our number system and for almost all of the number work in the primary grades. It involves more than just knowing the number names, their sequence, and how to write each number. While it may seem simple, counting is actually quite complex and involves the interplay between a number of skills and concepts.

Rote Counting

Students need to know the number names and their order by rote; they learn this sequence—both forward and backward—by hearing others count and by counting themselves. However, just as saying the alphabet does not indicate that a student can use written language, being able to say "one, two, three, four, five, six, seven, eight, nine, ten" does not necessarily indicate that students know what those counting words mean. Students also need to use numbers in meaningful ways if they are to build an understanding of quantity and number relationships.

One-to-One Correspondence

To count accurately, a student must know that one number name stands for one object that is being counted. Often, when young children first begin to count, they do not connect the numbers in the "counting song" to the objects they are counting. Children learn about one-to-one correspondence through repeated opportunities to count sets of objects and to watch others as they count. One-to-one correspondence develops over time with students first counting small groups of objects (up to five or six) accurately, and eventually larger groups.

Keeping Track

Another important part of counting accurately is being able to keep track of what has already been counted and what remains to be counted. As students first learn to count sets of objects, they often count some objects more than once and skip other objects altogether. Students develop strategies for organizing and keeping track of a count as they realize the need and as they see others use such strategies.

Connecting Numbers to Quantities

Many young students are still coordinating the ordinal sequence of the numbers with the cardinal meaning of those numbers. In other words, we get to 5 by counting in order 1, 2, 3, 4, 5. Understanding this aspect of number is connected to the one-to-one correspondence between the numbers we say and the objects we are counting. However, being able to count accurately using this ordinal sequence is not the same as knowing that when we have finished counting, the final number in our sequence will tell us the quantity of the things we have counted.

Conservation

Conservation of number involves understanding that three is always three, whether it is three objects together, three objects spread apart, or some other formation. As students learn to count, you will see many who do not yet understand this idea. They think that the larger the arrangement of objects, the more objects there are. Being able to conserve quantity is not a skill that can be taught; it is a cognitive process that develops as children grow.

Counting by Groups

Counting a set of objects by equal groups such as 2s, requires that each of the steps mentioned above happens again, at a different level. Students need to know the 2s sequence (2, 4, 6, 8) by rote. They need to realize that one number in this count represents two objects, and that each time they say a number they are adding another group of two to their count. Keeping track while counting by groups becomes a more complex task as well. Students begin to explore counting by groups in the data unit, *Sorting and Surveys*, as they count the number of eyes in their class. However, most students will not count by groups in a meaningful way until first or second grade.

Observing Kindergarteners As They Count

In Kindergarten, you can expect to see a wide range of number skills within your class. Students in the same class can vary considerably in age and in their previous experience with numbers and counting.

Your students will have many opportunities to count and use numbers not only in this unit, but throughout the year. You can learn a great deal about what your students understand by observing them. Listen to students as they talk with one another. Observe them as they count orally, as they count objects, and as they use numerals to record. Ask them about their thinking. You may observe some of the following:

Counting Orally

By the end of the year, most kindergarteners will have learned to rote count to 20 and beyond, with some able to count as high as 100. Many will be able to count orally much higher than they can count objects. Many who have learned the internal counting pattern or sequence (1, 2, 3 . . . 21, 22, 23 . . .), will still find the "bridge" numbers into the next decade (such as 19, 20, or 29, 30) difficult. You may hear children count "twenty-eight, twenty-nine, twenty-ten." Just as the young child who says "I runned away" understands something about the regularities of the English language, the student who says "twenty-ten" understands something about the regularity of the counting numbers. Students gradually learn the bridge numbers as they hear and use the counting sequence.

Counting Quantities

Most kindergarteners end the year with a grasp of *quantities* up to 20 or so. Some students accurately count quantities above 20, while others may not consistently count smaller quantities. Some may be inconsistent and count successfully one time while having difficulty the next.

Even when students can accurately count the objects in a set, they may not know that the last number counted also describes the number of objects in the set. You may observe students who successfully count a set of cubes, but have to go back and recount the set to answer the question, "How many cubes are there?" These students have not yet connected the counting numbers to the quantity of objects in a set. Students develop their understanding of quantity through repeated experiences organizing and counting sets of objects. In Kindergarten, many of the activities that focus on quantity can be adjusted so that students are working at a level of challenge appropriate for them.

Organizing a Count

Some students may be able to count objects they can pick up, move around, and organize with far more accuracy than they can when counting static objects, such as pictures of things on a page. You may observe some students who can count objects correctly when the group is organized for them, but you will see others who have trouble organizing or keeping track of objects themselves. They will need many and varied experiences with counting to develop techniques for counting accurately and for keeping track of what they are counting.

Counting by Writing Numbers

Knowing how to write numerals is not directly related to counting and understanding quantity; however, it is useful for representing a quantity that has been counted. Young students who are learning how to write numerals frequently reverse numbers or digits. Often this is not a mathematical problem but a matter of experience. Students need many opportunities to see how numerals are formed and to practice writing them. They should gain this experience by using numbers to record mathematical information, such as the number of students in school today or the number of objects on a page of a counting book. Numeral formation is related to letter formation; both are important in order to communicate in writing. We recommend that rote practice of numeral writing be part of handwriting instruction rather than mathematics.

Creating Your Own Story Problems

Following are story problems you can use as you repeat the activity, Acting Out Story Problems, over the course of this unit.

Story Problems That Involve Combining

- Seven children were splashing in the swimming pool. Two more children got into the swimming pool, and they all splashed around together. (Then how many children were splashing in the swimming pool?)

- Eight birds were sitting on a tree branch, flapping their wings. Two more birds flew over to join them. (Then how many birds were on the tree branch?)

- Six children were jumping rope on the playground. Five more came and joined them. (Then how many children were jumping rope on the playground?)

- Heather had six toy cars. Noah gave her two more toy cars. (How many toy cars does Heather have now?)

- Santos had five shells. He found four more shells. (Now how many shells does Santos have?)

- On Monday, Clara took five books out of the library. On Tuesday, she took five more books out of the library. (How many books did Clara take out of the library in all?)

Story Problems That Involve Separating

- Eight children were digging in the sandbox. Three of the children went over to the swings. (How many children were left digging in the sandbox?)

- Eight snakes were slithering around in the grass. Four of the snakes slithered into a hole to sleep. (How many snakes were still slithering around in the grass?)

- Ten cats were sleeping on the kitchen floor. Two of the cats woke up and went outside. (How many cats were left sleeping on the kitchen floor?)

- Ginny had six grapes. She ate three of them. (Now how many grapes does she have?)

- Ahmad had five flowers. He gave four of them to Krista. (How many flowers did he have left?)

- Seven apples were hanging from a branch of an apple tree. Taniqua picked three of them. (How many apples were left on the branch of the tree?)

Many teachers prefer to create their own problems. This enables them to use story contexts that reflect the interests, knowledge, and environment of their own students, as well as to adjust the numbers appropriately.

Creating Interesting Contexts In creating, combining, and separating situations, use contexts that are familiar and interesting to students without being distracting. For example, you can change a problem about a class trip to a fire station to reflect a trip to a familiar place in your community. Teachers find that simple situations that are familiar to all their students are the most satisfying. One source of good situations is experiences that you know all your students have had. For example, one class walks to a nearby park every day for recess; a problem based on that experience might be:

When we were at the park today, I counted three birds on the ground and four more in a tree. How many birds did I see in the park?

Another class is taking a field trip:

We have two teachers and four parents coming with us on our field trip today. How many grown-ups are coming with us?

Sometimes teachers present stories about their students, being sure to use the name of each child in a story at some point. You can also make up two characters who have experiences very much like those of your students. Give them names or let the students name them, and build all of your problem situations around these characters.

Jana and Skye were drawing a big picture of rockets. Jana drew four rockets and Skye drew two rockets. How many rockets did they draw?

Jana and Skye went to the toy store. Jana bought four stickers and Skye bought two stickers. How many stickers did they buy?

Students seem to enjoy the consistency and familiarity of recurring characters.

You can also take advantage of special events, classroom happenings, seasons, or holidays for problem contexts.

If Jana made two snowballs and Skye made five, how many snowballs did they have?

Related Problems

Simple, familiar situations often suggest other problems that easily follow from the initial one. Such follow-up questions can be posed on the spot to students who need more challenge. Additional problems related to the previous examples might include the following:

Yesterday at the park, I counted six birds on the ground and two in the trees. Did I see more birds or fewer birds than I saw today?

Jana and Skye drew four more rockets. Now how many rockets are in their picture?

Jana and Skye gave away three of their stickers. How many did they have left?

Jana and Skye made four more snowballs. Then how many did they have?

Adjusting Numbers in the Problem

You will probably see wide variation in the numbers with which your students are comfortable working. Try to present problems at a medium level of challenge for most students. For problems that involve combining, totals from six up to ten or twelve are at the right level for many kindergarteners. Problems that involve separating are usually more difficult

for young students, so start with slightly smaller numbers—initial amounts up to seven or eight, with amounts of two, three, or four to be removed.

The problems in this unit follow these guidelines, but you may feel that these numbers are not appropriate for your students. Keep in mind that in this unit, students have experience with numbers in the teens and higher as they play these games *Double Compare, Collect 15 Together,* and their variations. The numbers in the story problems are deliberately small so that students can focus on making sense of the story, choosing appropriate solution strategies, and communicating these strategies in a way that others can understand. Although at times you may want to challenge students by giving them problems with larger numbers, you can also challenge them by asking them to find answers in more than one way and to find ways to explain their solution strategies more clearly.

Important Note on Problem Structure

In Kindergarten, students work with two familiar and simple problem structures: combining two amounts to find a total and removing one amount from another to find how much is left. There are many other story problem structures, varying widely in level of difficulty. When you change the context or numbers in a problem, be sure not to change the structure of the problem because this can significantly alter its level of difficulty. For example, this problem is at an appropriate level for many Kindergarten students:

I had six apples. I gave two apples to my sister. How many do I have left?

However, a change in problem structure can yield a much more difficult problem.

I have six apples. My sister has two apples. How many more apples do I have?

This second problem is likely to be too challenging for many kindergarteners.

Story Problems in Kindergarten

Presenting Story Problems

In order to solve story problems, young students first need to be able to think about the sequence of actions in the story. This is why much of the work with story problems in Kindergarten involves children picturing the story in their minds, retelling the story in their own words, and actually acting out the action of the story. Some teachers encourage students to close their eyes to help them concentrate, and others draw quick sketches of important words on the board to help students understand and imagine the story.

The goal of this work is to help students think about the actions in the stories and choose strategies that reflect those actions, rather than choose strategies because they have been told that the problem is of a certain type. By *not* telling students whether a story is about joining or taking away and not presenting it in a predictable sequence (i.e., always combining followed by separating), students must concentrate on the actions in the story to figure out how to solve it.

We suggest that teachers use words such as *combining* and *separating* in addition to words like *adding* and *subtracting*, because they emphasize the actions involved in the stories. These terms also take into account that students may solve problems in a variety of ways. For example, they may solve *separating* problems using strategies based on either subtraction (or counting back) or addition (or counting on).

We caution against overuse of the expression "take away" for subtraction. Although "take away" is one way to conceptualize a subtraction problem (and the only way it is presented in Kindergarten), students will encounter others types of situations in Grades 1 and 2 that are also modeled by subtraction equations. For example, the following are all possible story problems for $7 - 2 = 5$:

- I had 7, and Karen took away 2. Now how many do I have?

- I have 7 and Karen has 2. How many more do I have? (Or, how many fewer does Karen have?)

- I have 2 (or 5). How many more do I need to get to 7?

- How far is it from 2 to 7? (Or, what is the distance between 2 and 7?)

- I had 7. I lost some. Now I have 5. How many did I lose?

Sharing Strategies

There are always some students who are eager just to give an answer; teachers are encouraged to keep the emphasis on the solution strategies children use. In Kindergarten, you are likely to see a wide range:

For addition stories, some students will suggest counting out each group of people or objects in a story, and then counting them all, from one. Others will do the same thing, but use their fingers. Some will be ready to think about counting on, with objects, on their fingers, or in their heads. ("If there were 4, and then 3 more came, that's 5, 6, 7.") Some children might "just know" that 3 and 4 is 7, and a few will use combinations that they "just know" to solve other related problems; for example, "I know that 3 and 3 is 6, and 1 more makes 7."

Strategies you are likely to see for subtraction story problems include counting out the total number, removing some, and counting the number of objects remaining, or a similar but less typical strategy of counting back. Although some Kindergarten students may "just know" some addition combinations, they are less likely to be familiar with subtraction facts. However, they may use their knowledge of addition combinations to solve such a problem: "I know 2 and 5 make 7. You had 7 and dropped 2, so there has to be 5 left."

Discussions About the Operation

Another part of the story problem routine involves questions about the operations. Thinking about how stories are the same or different help students focus on what is special about the operations of addition and subtraction. Some students focus on how the quantities change: when you add you end up with more; subtraction situations leave you with less than the original number. In the words of a five- and six-year-old "[For combining stories] you get a bigger number than you started with." and "If you have [6] and you take some away, you will have less than [6]." Other students talk more about the actions in the stories. In one kind of story, 2 (or more) groups are put together, joined, or combined; the other type of story involves part of a group being taken away, separated, or lost.

Understand that it may be challenging for some kindergarteners to reason in this way. Over the next couple of years, as they solve a wide variety of story problems, they will gain an understanding of what kinds of actions suggest combining and what kinds suggest separating. They will also learn to consider relationships among the quantities in a story. This kind of thinking will enable them to tackle problems that involve larger numbers and more complex structures—problems that they may not be able to act out easily.

Assessing One More, One Fewer

By the end of this unit, students are expected to be able to figure out what is one more or one fewer than a number (Benchmark 3). Assessment Checklist: *One More, One Fewer* (M22) is included to help you keep track of your observations about students' strategies for figuring this out over the course of this Investigation and unit. What follows is a vignette from one teacher, describing what she learned about students' understanding of one more and one fewer as she observed them at work.

Students had already played a few games that asked them to add small amounts when they were introduced to One More, One Fewer.

Sarah and Dennis

I was curious what Sarah and Dennis would do with this activity because I know that they have trouble counting accurately past six. Dennis turned over a 5. Sarah rolled and said, "I got 1." Dennis pointed out that the cube actually said "plus 1." (He has told me that his mother gives him sheets with "pluses on them.") They looked confused, so I reviewed the rules of the game and asked Dennis to count out 5 pennies onto the Ten-Frame. When I asked how many pennies they would have if they took one more penny, Dennis quickly responded, "6." Sarah pointed out that it was her turn, took another penny, and counted: "1, 2, 3, 4, 5, 6."

Next, Sarah turned over an 8 and accurately counted out 8 pennies. Without rolling the Plus or Minus 1 Cube, Dennis added another penny, and counted them from 1. He lost track several times but recounted on his own. After several tries, he was able to count them accurately. Given the work both students needed with the counting, I decided to let them continue to play with just adding one penny each time. I made a note to check back with them in a day or so to see whether they were ready to also think about one fewer.

Mitchell

After watching Corey and Mitchell play for a while, I noticed that Mitchell kept looking at our number line. I was curious how he was using this tool. He told me, "When I roll one more I look to see the next number higher. When I roll this one [−1], I look to see the next number lower." This suggested to me that Mitchell understood that the next number in the counting sequence is "one more" (and vice versa).

Jack and Hugo

Jack and Hugo were playing slowly and carefully. One would turn over a card, count the number of objects on the card, and count out that number of pennies. Then, the other would roll the number cube and either add a penny or take one away, and then count all of the pennies again. It seemed pretty clear that they needed to recount the pennies each time to find the new total, but I was curious if this was true for all numbers or only for the numbers above six or seven. So, I asked, "What if you had a 2 on the card and then rolled one more? How many pennies would you have then?" Jack said, "That's easy. 3," and Hugo nodded in agreement. I asked, "What if the card said 5?" Both thought for a moment. Then Hugo counted out 5 pennies, Jack added one more, and they counted them together, announcing, "6!" I made a note to ask Jack and Hugo about 4 and 5 at a later time as I was interested in when they "just knew" one more and when they needed to count all.

Rebecca and Latoya

The first thing I noticed was that Rebecca and Latoya were not using the Ten-Frame. Instead, they flipped a card, rolled the cube, and then recorded. It was clear that they knew what was one more or one less for most, if not all, of the numbers under 10. I decided to give them a cube that included a +2 and −2 on it to provide more challenge. With this new cube, I noticed that they used the Ten-Frame. They would count on to add 2 pennies; if they rolled −2, they removed 2 pennies and then counted them from 1.

Mia

At first I thought Mia was counting on or back to find the total, but then I realized I was not quite correct. Whenever Mia rolled a +1 she counted on ("That's five, six."). When she rolled a −1 she removed a penny and counted all of the pennies again, from 1. At first I was a surprised that she consistently used two different strategies, but then I remembered how when I taught second grade, my students almost always had more sophisticated strategies for adding than for subtracting.

When I started taking notes about students' strategies, I was surprised how often these ideas came up outside One More, One Fewer. *(I was also surprised to see students who were fluent with* One More, One Fewer *count all to solve a problem about five marbles and one more. I guess the connection between the two was not as obvious to them as it was to me!) For example, one day I visited a group that was working on* Six Tiles in All *(page 129). I immediately noticed that a number of students were not working with 6 tiles. When I asked them how many tiles they were using, everyone responded "6." Since no one was checking his or her counts, I asked students how they were sure they had 6, and suggested counting to double-check.*

Victor was surprised to find that he had fewer than 6. He looked around for an extra, eyeing the pile of the student next to him. He didn't see any strays, so he took another tile from the bin and began making a new arrangement. I was surprised that he did not feel the need to count again, and asked him how he knew he needed one more. He replied, "Because we're supposed to have 6. I only had 5."

Beth double-checked her count by putting all of her tiles together and moving each tile to one side as she counted it. When she finished counting (at 7), she took one tile and put it back in the center of the table. She told me, "I had one too much." Then she recounted her tiles and, satisfied, began making new arrangements with them.

Seeing these ideas arise in other contexts made me think about other ways I can incorporate and assess these ideas. For example, I wonder what students will say if, after taking attendance tomorrow and sending Raul to the office with it, I ask, "We just took attendance and there were 18 students here today. But Raul just left the room. How many students do you think there are now? How could you figure that out?"

Although *One More, One Fewer* provides the clearest context for observing students' strategies, these concepts are embedded in many of the activities in this unit. Observe students as they play games with a 1, 2, 3 dot cube (*Collect 10, Collect 15, Roll and Record 2,* and *Build On*) and as they play *Build It/Change It* in Investigation 3. Watch what happens when only one of the counters is red (or yellow) in *Toss the Chips* in Investigation 4, or when seven blue tiles and one red are placed in the Counting Jar. Because these ideas come up in a variety of ways, you may want to write the name of the activity as you take notes on Assessment Checklist: *One More, One Fewer* (M22) to see whether students are successful across contexts.

Double Compare: Strategies for Combining and Comparing

Through the game of *Double Compare,* students develop strategies for combining two numbers and for reasoning about quantity. The following scenes from a classroom illustrate situations that commonly arise and show how to adjust the game for students at different levels.

Counting Objects

Students develop strategies for adding by drawing cards and combining the numbers on the cards.

As Jae turns up a 3 and a 0 and Sarah turns up two 8 cards, Jae begins by reminding himself, "Count those little things [the pictures on the cards]." Then, while Sarah watches, he counts each picture on the 3 card, touching them as he says the numbers. He announces that he has 3.

Sarah places her cards side by side, overlapping the edges. She counts slowly, touching all of the pictures as she says the numbers. However, she skips a few pictures, counts a few twice, and comes up with a total of 13. Jae says that he thinks 8 and 8 is 18. Although they are aware that at least one of these totals is inaccurate, they realize that regardless, Sarah's total is greater than Jae's total of 3, and they are ready to move on.

At this point the teacher steps in and asks them to recount Sarah's total, slowly. After a couple of trials, Sarah and Jae both come up with a total of 16. The teacher suggests that they use interlocking cubes to help them find the totals on their cards. Because cubes, unlike the pictures on the cards, can be moved around, they can make it easier for students to keep track of what they have counted and what they have left to count.

Sarah and Jae both need to count by ones to be sure of their totals, and counting totals greater than 10 is challenging for them. The teacher plans to return in a few minutes to see whether the cubes are helpful. If Sarah and Jae are still having difficulty working with larger numbers, she will suggest that they play with only the 1–6 cards. Later in the session, she will call together students having difficulty and will work with them as they play *Double Compare.*

Counting and Counting On

Manuel's cards   Dennis's cards

Manuel and Dennis get right to work finding their totals. Dennis counts quietly to himself. He begins at 9, and then counts "10, 11, 12, 13, 14." With each number he says, Dennis uses his right index finger to bend back one of the fingers on his left hand. When he has bent back all of the fingers on his left hand, he stops counting and announces that he has 14.

Meanwhile, Manuel is still counting. He began by looking first at the 7 card and counting from one to seven. Then, he turned to the 4 card and began counting "8, 9, . . ." When Dennis announced his total of 14, Manuel lost his place. He begins counting again. He counts to seven, and then he counts the pictures on the 4 card, saying "8" as he points to the first picture, "9" as he points to the second, and so on, until he reaches 11. The boys agree that Dennis has the greater total. Like Sarah, Manuel puts the two quantities together and counts them all, starting at one. Dennis can begin with one quantity and count on, starting with the next number. In order to do this, Dennis treats nine as a unit; that is, he can think of it as nine without breaking it down into ones again. Then, he counts on— "10, 11, 12, 13, 14"—while keeping track with his fingers of how many he needs to add (1, 2, 3, 4, 5). The teacher believes that the game is at an appropriate level of challenge for Dennis and Manuel. In future sessions, she will observe them to see how their strategies for counting and combining are developing. For example, she will note whether Manuel continues counting from one each time and whether they have begun developing strategies for determining particular combinations without counting.

"Just Knowing" Number Combinations

Latoya's cards   Lisa's cards

As Latoya and Lisa turn over their cards, Latoya immediately announces that she has 15, and then looks over at Lisa's cards. The teacher reminds Latoya to let Lisa find her own total. Meanwhile, Lisa counts almost inaudibly to herself "10, 11, 12," and then says that her total is 12. Latoya says, "Me! I won."

How did you get your totals?

Latoya: Because I know eight and seven make 15. Because it's easy.

On the next round, Latoya again immediately announces her total, and then waits impatiently while Lisa slowly counts on from nine.

When the teacher again asks how the girls found their solutions, Latoya is still unable to explain. She seems either to have memorized some number combinations or to have developed strategies for finding solutions to number combinations quickly. Latoya is eager to play at a faster pace than she can with Lisa, so the teacher decides to ask her to play with Russell, who is also finding number combinations quickly. To provide further challenge, she may ask Latoya and Russell to turn over three cards on a round.

Reasoning About Number Combinations

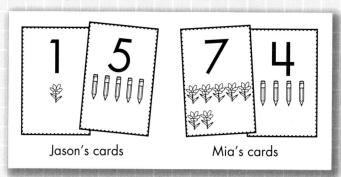

Jason's cards   Mia's cards

Jason: 1 and 5 is 6. I have 6.

Mia: 8, 9, . . . [*after a short pause*] Me! Because you have 6 and I have more.

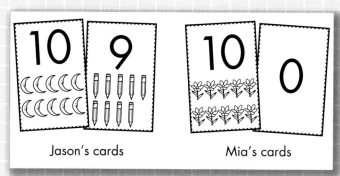

Jason's cards   Mia's cards

Jason: Me! 9 is bigger than 0. You know because it's just your eyes that tell you.

Mia and Jason are reasoning about the number pairs without necessarily needing to add them up. Although the teacher has observed in previous sessions that Jason and Mia are skilled at counting, combining, and comparing numbers, she believes that this game is deepening their understanding of numbers and number relationships as they explore ways to reason about numbers.

Choosing a Card to Win a Round

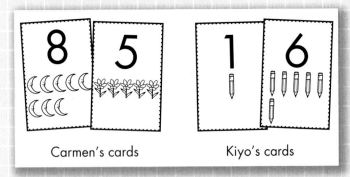

Carmen's cards   Kiyo's cards

Carmen and Kiyo count together slowly, starting with Carmen's cards. Carmen touches the pictures as she counts. Kiyo tells her that she has counted a picture twice, and they begin again. After several trials, they complete the count with a total of 12.

Kiyo: 6 and 1 is 7. But it's my turn to win this time . . . [She places her cards side by side so that the one is to the left of the six.] It's 16. I win!

They both laugh, knowing that the pictures can be combined to find the total number but the digits cannot be combined in that way.

Next, Kiyo removes her 1 card and places it facedown in her discard pile. She pulls out a 3 card from her pile and then returns it, saying "Three, too small." Then, she pulls out a 2 card from her pile, hesitates, and puts it back, saying "I need something big." Finally, she pulls out a 9, and puts it face up with the 6.

Kiyo: There. It's bigger than your 12. I won.

Carmen: OK. My turn to win next.

Carmen and Kiyo have invented a version of *Double Compare* in which players win alternate rounds. If the player whose turn it is to win has a losing hand, she can choose a replacement card. Although Carmen and Kiyo appear to need more practice counting and combining (they struggled to combine 8 and 5 and arrived at an incorrect total), the teacher decides not to intervene at this point. Although they are not always finding the total of their combinations correctly, they are nonetheless gaining practice counting, comparing, and combining. They are concentrating fully on their work and, as they find winning combinations, they are reasoning about the relative size of numbers and number combinations. The teacher compliments them on developing a collaborative version of the game.

Dialogue Box

Measuring with Sticks

These students have been using craft sticks to measure the length of adding machine tape strips around the room. At the end of Session 1.5, the teacher gathers students around one strip to discuss the strategies they have been using. Notice how she asks students to demonstrate and discuss different strategies, rather than showing or telling them how to measure.

Teacher: Today I want to talk about how you have been using the craft sticks to measure. Would someone show us how you would use craft sticks to measure this tape?

Dennis comes forward and lays out the sticks end to end but does not start at the beginning or stop at the end of the tape.

Dennis: There. 1, 2, 3, 4, 5, 6; it's 6 sticks long.

Teacher: How did you decide how to line up the sticks?

Dennis: I put them on the tape and that's how many I can put: 6.

Kiyo: But you have to start at one end and end at the other.

Teacher: Kiyo, would you do it differently? [Kiyo nods.] Would you show us?

Kiyo lines up the first stick with one end of the tape. She lays the sticks on top of the tape but leaves gaps between them. When the last stick extends beyond the end of the tape, she takes away one of the middle sticks and readjusts the final stick so that the end aligns with the end of the tape. She readjusts the middle sticks so that they cover the tape but are not touching end to end.

Teacher: Kiyo, can you tell us about your strategy?

Kiyo: The sticks have to start at this end of the tape and they have to end at the other end, so I fixed them to make that happen. There are 4 sticks.

Tammy: But she's got holes. Kiyo, squish them together so they touch. Can I show you? [Kiyo nods. Tammy comes up to the tape, eliminates the gaps between the sticks, and adds one more to the end of the line.]

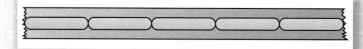

Tammy: There. It's 5.

The teacher asks other students to comment on the strategies they have seen and the importance of starting/ending points and placing the sticks end-to-end. Such discussions develop students' understanding of length as the distance between two points, including all of the space between. The teacher encourages students to modify and readjust their strategies and ends with a question aimed at another big idea:

Teacher: When Dennis measured the tape, he got 6 craft sticks. Kiyo got 4, and Tammy thinks it's 5. Can this strip of adding machine tape be 4 *or* 5 *or* 6 craft sticks long? Does it matter that we got three different measurements?

The teacher poses this question knowing that, just as some students can conserve quantities and know that 5 is 5 whether it is in a small pile or stretched out in a line, some of her students understand that the measurements should be the same if you are using the same tool to measure a given length. Others are not yet sure of this. These students need many opportunities to measure, to watch others as they measure, and to discuss measurement techniques and the reasoning behind them.

How Many Fish in All?

Several students have just acted out the following story for the class:

When I went to a pond the other day, I saw three little fish swimming in the water. While I watched, three other little fish came to join them.

The actors remain in front of the group while the teacher asks the class to share ways they could find how many fish in all are in the pond. Students suggest strategies that involve counting people, counting on their fingers, and using knowledge of number combinations. Throughout the discussion, the teacher encourages students to focus on solution strategies, rather than on the solution itself.

Teacher: Who has a way to tell how many fish there are in all?

Brad: 6.

Teacher: Can you tell us how you got 6?

Brad: There were 3, and I counted 4, 5, 6.

Teacher: Who else has a way to tell how many fish there are in all?

Various students: 6! 7! 8!

Teacher: It seems that we have some different ideas about how many fish in all. What could we do to figure this out?

Victor: Each person who's a fish could say a number and then go back to their seat.

Mia: When you say your number, you could sit down on the floor. Then you could see who was counted.

Latoya: I knew there were 6 because I added those numbers when I was four years old.

Teacher: Does anyone have another way?

Rebecca: 3 and 3. You can count your fingers.

Teacher: Let's try it. What are the numbers in the story? Show me with your hands. What numbers are you holding up?

Students: 3 and 3.

Teacher: Let's count. [The class counts the fingers they are holding up together and arrive at a total of 6.] Let's also try Victor's way. When I point to you, say your number and go back to your seat. [The students who acted the part of fish count off in this way. The class cheers as the last one says "6."]

A student uses her fingers to show how many fish there are in all.

Dialogue Box

How Are These Stories Different?

Students have acted out and shared solution strategies for each of the following story problems:

Four bees were buzzing around a flower. Three more bees were at the hive. They flew over to join the others at the flower. (Then how many bees were buzzing around the flower?)

Now there were seven bees buzzing around the flower. Two bees left the flower and flew back to the hive. (How many bees were still buzzing around the flower?)

The teacher asks students to think about how the two stories are different.

Teacher: We just solved two problems about bees. In the first one, four bees were at the flower, and three more came and joined them. In the second one, seven bees were at the flower, and two flew away. How are the stories different? Who has an idea?

Jason: Some bees went away, and in the other story, the bees came and joined.

Teacher: Can you tell us what you mean by "joined"?

Jason: It's like when you put things together.

Carmen: It's like a puzzle. You put it together.

Teacher: In the first story, two groups of bees joined together, and in the second, one group of bees went away. Who else has another idea about how the two stories are different?

Kaitlyn: They have different numbers.

Teacher: Different numbers? Can you say more about that?

Raul: There was four and three, and there was seven and two.

Tammy: At first there were seven bees, and then there were only five because two flew away.

Teacher: There were fewer bees at the end of the second story because some bees left to go back to the hive. Were there fewer bees at the end of the first story, when some bees came and joined the group at the flower?

Tammy: No, there were three and then four came, and that's seven.

Note that throughout the discussion, the teacher follows up students' comments about the kinds of actions and the relationships among quantities in the stories. In this way, she begins to draw attention to which actions suggest combining and which suggest separating. The teacher points out that when quantities are combined, the result is more, whereas when they are separated, the result is fewer.

It Looks Like a Chair

After working to generate and record different arrangements of 6 tiles in Session 4.1, students are now meeting to share some of their work. After each student shares a design, the teacher chooses one, an L shape, to talk about how students could remember it.

Teacher: Take a minute to look at and think about Emma's arrangement. What do you notice?

Victor: It has greens and yellows.

Lisa: There's a pattern [pointing]: green, yellow, green, yellow, green, yellow.

Teacher: Victor and Lisa noticed the colors in Emma's pattern and how the colors were arranged. How else could you remember this pattern?

Brad: It looks like a L.

Victor: There's 6. 1, 2, 3, 4, 5, 6.

Tammy: I think it looks like a chair.

Raul: Or a leg and a foot.

Tammy: There are 3 up and down [holds up three fingers on one hand], and then there are 3 across on the bottom [holds up three fingers on the other hand]. That's 6.

Teacher: How do you know that there are 6?

Tammy: [touching each finger to her chin as she counts]: 1, 2, 3, 4, 5, 6.

Teacher: Did you see what Tammy used to figure that out? She used her fingers. I've noticed many of you using your fingers to count and keep track.

Students examine the different shapes that arrangements of six tiles can make.

Different Ways to See a Shape

In this discussion, which happens in Session 4.7, students are sharing the ways they think about one classmate's arrangement of 6 tiles. Some talk about the overall shape, others break the image into smaller parts, and still others are beginning to think of the number of squares in each part. The teacher accepts all responses but follows up opportunities that arise to encourage students to use numbers in their descriptions.

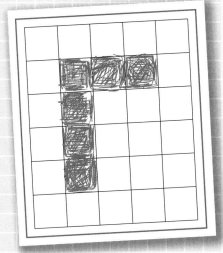

Kiyo's Work

Teacher: Kiyo, what can you tell us about your shape?

Kiyo: It's a hoe, an upside-down hoe. I worked in the garden today.

Corey: I think it looks like a droopy sunflower.

Lisa: It kind of looks like a 7, but it's not going the right way, so it's not really a 7, but it looks a little like a 7.

Kiyo: It's not a 7. It has six squares.

Lisa: But it looks like a 7.

Teacher: Kiyo, you said that it has 6 squares. How can you tell it has 6?

Kiyo: I did this for 6 in my book. [She holds up her page.] I put a circle around these four and wrote "4" because there are 4 tiles going down. And then I did two for these because there are 2 for the hoe part.

Russell: What's the hoe part?

Kiyo: That's the part that digs; the other part is the handle.

Teacher: Kiyo thought of this shape as having one part with 4 and one part with 2. Is there another way we can think about this shape? [Pause.] Is there another way you can think about the parts of the shape, like when we do *Quick Images?*

Abby: There's 3 and 3.

Teacher: Could you say more about that? What's 3?

Abby: It goes 3 over and then 3 down. 1, 2, 3 [indicates the top three squares], then down [points down the vertical column] it's 1, 2, 3.

Russell: I have another idea. I think it can be two things. It can be 4 and 2, and I think it can be 3 and 3.

Teacher: That is interesting. It's the same shape, but we can call it 4 and 2 and we can call it 3 and 3. Any other ways you can see the picture? . . . You came up with so many ways to see the picture. A hoe, a sunflower, a group of 4 and a group of 2, a group of 3 and a group of 3, and a 7—even though it has 6 tiles!

Student Math Handbook

The *Student Math Handbook Flip Chart* pages related to this unit are pictured on the following pages. This book is designed to be used flexibly: as a resource for providing visual prompts for the teacher to use when introducing a new math activity or idea, as a resource for reviewing math words and ideas with students, and as a resource for students to use as they are doing classwork.

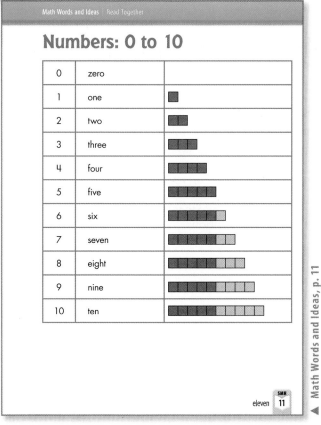

Numbers: 0 to 10

0	zero	
1	one	
2	two	
3	three	
4	four	
5	five	
6	six	
7	seven	
8	eight	
9	nine	
10	ten	

eleven SMH 11

▲ Math Words and Ideas, p. 11

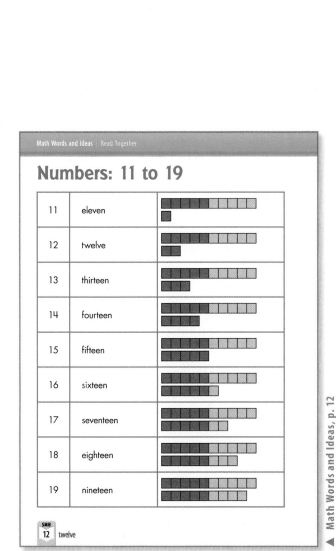

Numbers: 11 to 19

11	eleven	
12	twelve	
13	thirteen	
14	fourteen	
15	fifteen	
16	sixteen	
17	seventeen	
18	eighteen	
19	nineteen	

SMH 12 twelve

▲ Math Words and Ideas, p. 12

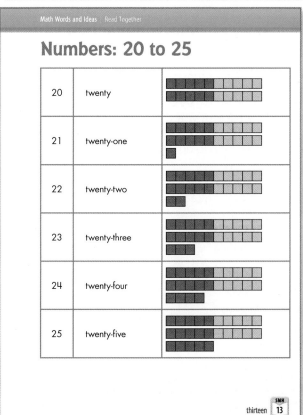

Numbers: 20 to 25

20	twenty	
21	twenty-one	
22	twenty-two	
23	twenty-three	
24	twenty-four	
25	twenty-five	

thirteen SMH 13

▲ Math Words and Ideas, p. 13

Panel 1 (top left)

Numbers: 26 to 30

26	twenty-six	
27	twenty-seven	
28	twenty-eight	
29	twenty-nine	
30	thirty	

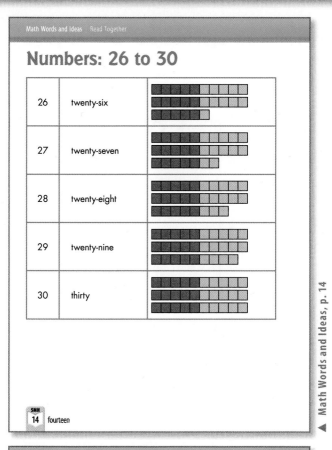

Panel 2 (top right)

More Counting

How many students are here today?

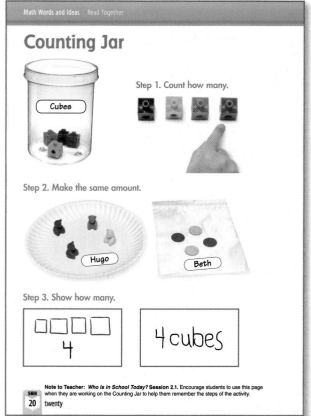

20 students are here today.

? **How many students are in your class?**

Note to Teacher: *Who Is in School Today?* **Session 1.1.** Use this page to show that we use numbers both to count a set of objects (1, 2, 3, . . . 20) and to describe the quantity of those objects (the total is 20).

Panel 3 (bottom left)

Ways to Count

When you count, you say one number for each object. You need to keep track of what you are counting.

The last number you say is the total. The total tells you how many are in the group.

Look at how some children count.

Jack puts each button in a cup as he counts it.	 Three . . .
Abby moves each button as she counts it.	 Four . . .
Kiyo puts the buttons in a row to count them.	 Eight . . .

? **What do you do when you count?**

Note to Teacher: *Who Is in School Today?* **Session 2.5.** Use these examples in your first discussion about strategies for counting the objects in the Counting Jar and whenever you discuss how students count.

Panel 4 (bottom right)

Counting Jar

Cubes

Step 1. Count how many.

Step 2. Make the same amount.

Hugo   Beth

Step 3. Show how many.

4

4 cubes

Note to Teacher: *Who Is in School Today?* **Session 2.1.** Encourage students to use this page when they are working on the Counting Jar to help them remember the steps of the activity.

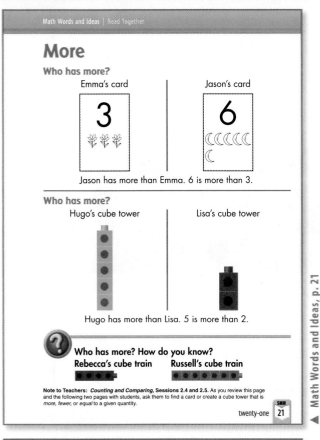

More

Who has more?

Emma's card

Jason's card

3

6

Jason has more than Emma. 6 is more than 3.

Who has more?

Hugo's cube tower

Lisa's cube tower

Hugo has more than Lisa. 5 is more than 2.

? **Who has more? How do you know?**

Rebecca's cube train   Russell's cube train

Note to Teachers: *Counting and Comparing,* Sessions 2.4 and 2.5. As you review this page and the following two pages with students, ask them to find a card or create a cube tower that is *more, fewer,* or *equal* to a given quantity.

SMH 21   twenty-one

◄ Math Words and Ideas, p. 21

Fewer

Who has fewer?

Jae's card

Kaitlyn's card

4

8

Jae has fewer than Kaitlyn. 4 is less than 8.

Who has fewer?

Tammy's cube tower

Mitchell's cube tower

Mitchell has fewer than Tammy. 3 is less than 6.

? **Who has fewer?**

Carmen's cube train   Kyle's cube train

Note to Teachers: *Counting and Comparing,* Sessions 2.4 and 2.5. As you review this page, the previous page, and the following page with students, ask them to find a card or create a cube tower that is *more, fewer,* or *equal* to a given quantity.

SMH 22   twenty-two

◄ Math Words and Ideas, p. 22

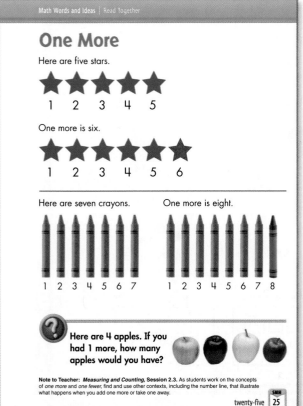

One More

Here are five stars.

★ ★ ★ ★ ★
1 2 3 4 5

One more is six.

★ ★ ★ ★ ★ ★
1 2 3 4 5 6

Here are seven crayons.   One more is eight.

1 2 3 4 5 6 7   1 2 3 4 5 6 7 8

? Here are 4 apples. If you had 1 more, how many apples would you have?

Note to Teacher: *Measuring and Counting,* Session 2.3. As students work on the concepts of *one more* and *one fewer,* find and use other contexts, including the number line, that illustrate what happens when you add one more or take one away.

SMH 25   twenty-five

◄ Math Words and Ideas, p. 25

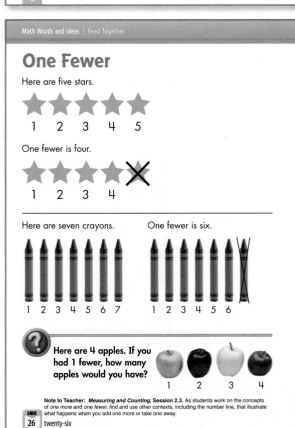

One Fewer

Here are five stars.

★ ★ ★ ★ ★
1 2 3 4 5

One fewer is four.

★ ★ ★ ★ ✗
1 2 3 4

Here are seven crayons.   One fewer is six.

1 2 3 4 5 6 7   1 2 3 4 5 6

? Here are 4 apples. If you had 1 fewer, how many apples would you have?

1 2 3 4

Note to Teacher: *Measuring and Counting,* Session 2.3. As students work on the concepts of *one more* and *one fewer,* find and use other contexts, including the number line, that illustrate what happens when you add one more or take one away.

SMH 26   twenty-six

◄ Math Words and Ideas, p. 26

Five Tiles

These students are looking at this arrangement of 5 tiles.

Here's how they know that there are 5.

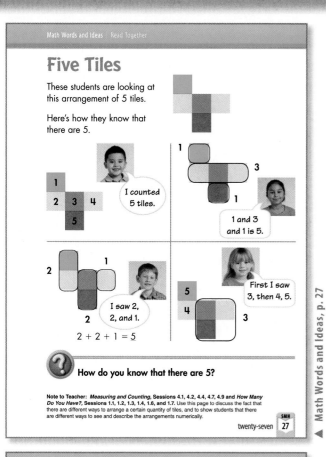

I counted 5 tiles.

1 and 3 and 1 is 5.

I saw 2, 2, and 1.

2 + 2 + 1 = 5

First I saw 3, then 4, 5.

How do you know that there are 5?

Note to Teacher: *Measuring and Counting*, Sessions 4.1, 4.2, 4.4, 4.7, 4.9 and *How Many Do You Have?*, Sessions 1.1, 1.2, 1.3, 1.4, 1.6, and 1.7. Use this page to discuss the fact that there are different ways to arrange a certain quantity of tiles, and to show students that there are different ways to see and describe the arrangements numerically.

twenty-seven

SMH 27

◀ Math Words and Ideas, p. 27

Ways to Make 6

There are different ways to make a number.
Here are some ways to make 6.

Toss the Chips

These students tossed 6 two-color counters.
Some landed on the red side. Some landed on the yellow side.

3 red and 3 yellow | 2 red and 4 yellow

Six Tiles

These students arranged 6 tiles.

3 and 3 | 2 and 2 and 2 | 3 and 3

1 and 5 | 1 and 2 and 3

Can you think of another way to make 6?

Note to Teacher: *How Many Do You Have?*, Session 4.6. Use these pages to help students see that there are certain combinations that make a number, no matter which material they are using or what game they are playing. Encourage students to find combinations that appear more than once.

SMH 28 twenty-eight

◀ Math Words and Ideas, p. 28

A Library Story Problem

Here is a story about children at a library.

Three children were reading books at the library.

Then two more children came to the library to read.

What happened in this story?

Was this story about putting groups together or about taking away part of a group?

Note to Teacher: *How Many Do You Have?*, Sessions 3.3 and 3.5. After reviewing this page and the following three pages, ask students to visualize, act out, and solve these story problems, as well as the others you create.

thirty-one

SMH 31

◀ Math Words and Ideas, p. 31

Solving a Library Story Problem

Here's the story.

There were 3 children reading books at the library.
Then 2 more children came to the library to read.
How many children in all were reading at the library?
Here are some ways students solved this problem.

These students acted out the story.

1, 2, 3; 4, 5

Mia used cubes.

1   2   3

4   5

I took 3 cubes. Then I took 2 more cubes. Then I counted them.

Jack drew a picture.

I drew the kids. 3 and 2 is 5.

How would you solve the problem?

Note to Teacher: *How Many Do You Have?*, Sessions 3.3 and 3.5. After reviewing this page, the previous page, and the following two pages, ask students to visualize, act out, and solve these story problems, as well as others you create.

SMH 32 thirty-two

◀ Math Words and Ideas, p. 32

A Story Problem About Books

Here is a story about books.
Corey was looking for books in the library.
She saw 5 books on the table.

Corey took 2 of the books from the table to read.
What happened in this story?

? **Was this story about putting groups together or about taking away part of a group?**

Note to Teacher: *How Many Do You Have?*, **Sessions 3.3 and 3.5.** After reviewing this page, the previous two pages, and the following page, ask students to visualize, act out, and solve these story problems, as well as others you create.

SMH 33 thirty-three

▲ Math Words and Ideas, p. 33

Solving a Story Problem About Books

Corey was looking for books in the library.
She saw 5 books on the table.
Corey took 2 of the books from the table to read.
How many books were left on the table?

These students acted out the story.

1, 2, 3

Manuel used cubes.

I put 5 cubes together.

1 2 3

1 2 3 4 5

Then I took off 2 cubes and counted the cubes left.

Cindy drew a picture.

I drew 5 books. Then I crossed out 2 books and counted how many books were left.

? **How would you solve the problem?**

Note to Teacher: *How Many Do You Have?*, **Sessions 3.3 and 3.5.** After reviewing this page and the previous three pages, ask students to visualize, act out, and solve these story problems, as well as the others you create.

SMH 34 thirty-four

▲ Math Words and Ideas, p. 34

Measurement

You can measure to find out . . .

Who is taller?

How big is my shoe?

How long is the table?

? **What else can you measure?**

Note to Teacher: *Measuring and Counting*, **Investigation 1.** Use this page to facilitate a discussion about the many purposes of measurement.

SMH 36 thirty-six

▲ Math Words and Ideas, p. 36

Measuring with Cubes

These students used cubes to measure the length of some objects in their classroom.

This book is 13 cubes long.

This comb is 7 cubes long.

? **How long is the shoe?**

Note to Teacher: *Measuring and Counting*, **Session 1.2.** Students can consider these examples of using cubes to measure objects. Ask them to compare the lengths. Which object is the longest? Which is the shortest?

SMH 38 thirty-eight

▲ Math Words and Ideas, p. 38

Index